Rees

Understanding Injection Molding Technology

Hanser **Understanding** Books
A Series of Mini-Tutorials

Series Editor: E.H. Immergut

Understanding Injection Molding Technology (Rees)
Understanding Polymer Morphology (Woodward)

In Preparation:

Understanding Mold Design (Gerson)
Understanding Quality Systems for Polymer Processing (Keating)
Understanding Adhesion and Adhesives Technology (Pocius)

Herbert Rees

Understanding
Injection Molding Technology

Hanser Publishers, Munich Vienna New York

Hanser/Gardner Publications, Inc., Cincinnati

The Author:
Herbert Rees, 248386-5 Side Road (Mono), RR#5 Orangeville, Ontario, Canada L9W 2Z2

Distributed in the USA and in Canada by
Hanser/Gardner Publications, Inc.
6600 Clough Pike, Cincinnati, Ohio 45244-4090, USA
Fax: +1 (513) 527-8950

Distributed in all other countries by
Carl Hanser Verlag
Postfach 86 04 20, 81631 München, Germany
Fax: +49 (89) 98 48 09

The use of general descriptive names, trademarks, etc., in this publication, even if the former are not especially identified, is not to be taken as a sign that such names, as understood by the Trade Marks and Merchandise Marks Act, may accordingly be used freely by anyone.

While the advice and information in this book are believed to be true and accurate at the date of going to press, neither the authors nor the editors nor the publisher can accept any legal responsibility for any errors or omissions that may be made. The publisher makes no warranty, express or implied, with respect to the material contained herein.

Library of Congress Cataloging-in-Publication Data
Rees, Herbert, 1915–
Understanding injection molding technology / Herbert Rees.
   p. cm.
Includes bibliographical references and index.
ISBN 1-56990-130-9
1. Injection molding of plastics.   I. Title.
TP1150.R45   1994
668.4'12--dc20   94-10078

Die Deutsche Bibliothek-CIP-Einheitsaufnahme
Rees, Herbert:
Understanding injection molding technology / Herbert Rees. -
Munich ; Vienna ; New York : Hanser ; Cincinnati :
Hanser/Gardner, 1994
   (Understanding)

© Carl Hanser Verlag, Munich Vienna New York, 1994
Typeset in the USA by pageAbility, Willseyville
Printed and bound in Germany by Schoder Druck GmbH & Co. KG, Gersthofen

Introduction to the Series

In order to keep up in today's world of rapidly changing technology we need to open our eyes and ears and, most importantly, our minds to new scientific ideas and methods, new engineering approaches and manufacturing technologies and new product design and applications. As students graduate from college and either pursue academic polymer research or start their careers in the plastics industry, they are exposed to problems, materials, instruments and machines that are unfamiliar to them. Similarly, many working scientists and engineers who change jobs must quickly get up to speed in their new environment.

To satisfy the needs of these "newcomers" to various fields of polymer science and plastics engineering, we have invited a number of scientists and engineers, who are experts in their field and also good communicators, to write short, introductory books which let the reader "understand" the topic rather than to overwhelm him/her with a mass of facts and data. We have encouraged our authors to write the kind of book that can be read profitably by a beginner, such as a new company employee or a student, but also by someone familiar with the subject, who will gain new insights and a new perspective.

Over the years this series of **Understanding** books will provide a library of mini-tutorials on a variety of fundamental as well as technical subjects. Each book will serve as a rapid entry point or "short course" to a particular subject and we sincerely hope that the readers will reap immediate benefits when applying this knowledge to their research or work-related problems.

E.H. Immergut
Series Editor

Preface

Understanding Injection Molding Technology describes in broad outlines the origin and processing of earlier plastics and how injection molding evolved. It presents in easily understood language an outline of injection molding technology, explaining how injection molding machines and molds work and describing the basic elements of injection molds and the various molding techniques used in the past and today.

Understanding Injection Molding Technology is intended to be read by anyone who is interested in plastics technology because of his or her association with the plastics molding industry. It will introduce the reader to the basic technical information needed to understand the injection molding process and will, therefore, be especially useful to "newcomers" to this industry. However, the book should also be of value to sales and/or customer service personnel, to buyers, molding machine operators, moldmakers and mechanics. It will make them understand the functions and the requirements of molding machines and molds. The book is also intended for students enrolled in plastics courses in order to give them an overview of the injection molding industry.

It is the author's hope that he has succeeded in demystifying the subject of injection molding technology and that the reader will now have a clearer picture of this important segment of the plastics processing industry.

Herbert Rees
Orangeville, Ontario

Contents

1 Introduction to Plastics Technology

1.1 Introduction

The purpose of this book is to familiarize the newcomer to the plastics industry and the field of injection molding technology with the elements and the terminology that will be encountered when working either as a technician, designer, engineer, or salesperson. This manual is not a complete and detailed account of all areas of the field but is rather intended to point out some of the various technical problems faced when working in this industry. It is also not a design manual for the aspiring engineer or technician wishing to enter this field. However, once the main points and concerns of each element are understood, a designer will be much better equipped to appreciate existing designs. Of course, one learns much more by actual hands-on experiences once exposed to the day-to-day problems and will eventually come forward with improvements and new ideas.

A serious student of any particular area must gather more information from the various books, magazines, and other literature. There are numerous textbooks covering various fields of plastics technology, most of which treat their subjects with highly theoretical and mathematical analyses. These books are certainly very valuable and often lead to solutions of the various problems encountered, but they often become lost in details which, while theoretically correct, may not have much significance in applications. However, anyone serious in studying a specific field must go through some of these texts.

1.2 Background and History of Plastics

Before addressing the subject of injection molding itself, we will first describe some of the background and history of plastics and the plastics technology to the present day. The word "plastic" derives from the Greek words for moldable and pliable. In modern usage, plastics almost always denotes organic polymers, usually including added materials such as colorants, lubricants, plasticizers, etc. The German term is *Kunstharz,* meaning synthetic resin, or *Kunststoffe,* which translates as artificial (synthetic) material. However, glass, concrete, and steel are also artificial materials but are inorganic and, therefore, not grouped with plastics.

A polymer is a substance made of giant molecules formed by the bonding of simple molecules; such molecules capable of forming polymers are "monomers". The polymers of interest herein are formed by two processes: polymerization and condensation. For example, molecules of ethylene bond to form a chainlike structure—polyethylene—by polymerization. Phenol and formaldehyde condense into phenol-formaldehyde resin (while splitting off water). Similarly, ethylene terephthalate condenses into polyethylene terephthalate (PET).

Polymers are identified by the prefix "poly" added to the name of the monomers. Not all polymers are made of the same molecules. Polystyrene (PS) is a polymer of the styrene molecule, but polyacrylostyrene (SAN) is a polymer of acrylonitrile and styrene and is designated a "copolymer".

The Society of the Plastics Industry, Inc. (SPI) prescribes a standard for the designation of plastics based on the name of the monomer from which they are obtained. Several examples are listed below:

ABS	Polyacrylobutadiene styrene
AN	Polyacrylonitrile
PC	Polycarbonate
PE	Polyethylene
PET	Polyethylene terephthalate
PP	Polypropylene
PS	Polystyrene
PVC	Polyvinylchloride
PVDC	Polyvinylidene chloride
SAN	Polyacrylostyrene

A polymer becomes a molding compound by the addition of substances to make it moldable and to improve its properties. Many additives are used to impart the desired physical, chemical, and electrical properties and to provide color and other effects, as shown in the following examples:

Lubricants—to improve flow during molding
Stabilizers—to prevent decomposition during heating
Dyes—to color the polymer
Antistatic agents

Radiation filters—(e.g., for ultraviolet)
Mold release agents
Fillers—to reduce the amount of expensive polymer in a given part
Foaming agents
Fire retardants
Reinforcing agents—(e.g., glass fibers)

1.2.1 History

Plastics were first created at the beginning of this century to replace natural materials, such as ivory, horn, silk, and rubber, which could not be produced in sufficient amounts to satisfy the ever-increasing demand. New industries such as the motion pictures required special materials (e.g., films) which did not yet exist. Chemists took up the challenge and started to create materials to satisfy special demands and to gradually replace the existing, often hard-to-get, and expensive natural materials. Eventually, these materials were not only replaced but improved upon with regard to quality, availability, and cost.

The next step was to develop successful applications that could replace zinc, aluminum, and steel, taking advantage of the lower weights, and result in cost savings in manufacturing. Later, more new materials were (and still are being) generated, often as fallout from space research, with properties not previously required or even known. The bases (feed stocks) for these artificial materials are all substances available in ample supply, such as petroleum gas and oil, coal, and cellulose.

The ease of processing, the availability, the relatively low cost, and the many special properties that could be designed into plastics created a revolution in everyday living. Consider the following examples:

• Cotton and wool were supplemented or replaced by acetates, acrylics, polyesters, PVC, PP, and others in the textile industry.
• Silk gave way to Nylon.
• Rubber was replaced by butyl and other polymers for tires, etc., and by PVC for records and as insulating material for electric wires.
• Glues (previously derived from bones) are now mostly made from thermosets.
• Porcelain dishware is often replaced by urea and melamine formaldehyde for more durable products and by PS and other compounds for "disposables".
• Zinc, aluminum, and steel gave way to Nylon, Delrin, polyesters, and other, newer "engineering plastics" in automotive and many other technical uses.

- Wood is being replaced with plastic foam panels for furniture.
- Glass is often replaced by PE, PP, PVC, PC, and PET in bottles, jars, and other containers.
- Natural oils, lacquers, and waxes are giving way to acrylic paints and other synthetic coatings.
- Paper (in packaging) is often replaced by PE, PVC, and other plastics.
- Bricks are often substituted with vinyl siding on the exteriors of houses.

This list goes on and on. Still, there is a certain reluctance in some quarters to accept plastics as a genuine material, and often the original, "natural" materials still compete well with their plastic replacements or equivalents. There are, as yet, no equal substitutes for natural furs, although there are now very good imitations on the market. It is also sometimes hard to break customs. Who wants to drink expensive wine decanted from a plastic bottle? There are also, sometimes, quite legitimate complaints about the use of plastic because of its environmental impact. However, its opponents often ignore the fact that many earlier materials were sometimes just as much or even more objectionable than plastic. For instance, which is preferable on a beach: a broken glass bottle or a discarded plastic bottle?

Without plastics, much of the world's industry would come to a standstill: the electrical industry would be without insulators, the rolling mills without lubricants, and paper without waterproofing. The public would miss most of the materials that now provide shelter, preserve food, and provide clothing.

During the oil crisis of 1973, there was quite a battle over the amount of petroleum feed stocks required to make "all these plastics". However, it takes less energy to produce plastic than to produce its equivalent in glass or steel. Also, there is considerable savings in transporting goods made from or packaged in plastics as compared to other, conventional packaging. Finally, plastic permits "light weighting" of cars and airplanes for greatly improved fuel economy and increased payloads. Newly developed plastics, with reinforcements of glass and carbon fibers, start closing the strength gap between steel and plastics and permit its use not only for body parts (fenders, grilles, ornaments) but also for springs, drive shafts, connecting rods, wrist pins, etc., for even greater weight gains and cost savings.

There is also obsolescence in plastics. Some materials that once were in great demand are now hard to find, since better, safer, and cheaper materials have been developed. Examples include viscose and acetate for yarns and celluloid for films and toys.

As in any other industry, many mistakes were made in the beginning, resulting in defective products. Some were deplorable and gave all plastics a bad name. Examples include constantly breaking toys and easily melted household articles. While much of this could be ascribed to inexperience on the part of the product designers, the molders, and the materials suppliers, some was due to lack of responsibility on the part of the industry and to the absence of quality standards.

Now, due to the practical experience gained over the last 70 years and exploration and research in industrial laboratories and at specialized universities, there is knowledge enough to make the plastics industry the fastest growing segment of materials technology and usage.

1.3   Types of Plastics

There are two basic groups of plastic materials: thermosets and thermoplastics. Thermosets are plastics in which the chemistry changes during processing, usually due to the application of heat and pressure, so that the finished product material is chemically different from the raw material. This change of chemistry is irreversible—that is, the material cannot be returned to its original state (e.g., by melting). Thermosets include the phenolics (one of the oldest plastics in the electrical industry, often called *Bakelite* after its inventor), ureas, melamines, alkyds, artificial rubbers, some glues, some paints, etc.

Thermoplastics are compounds which have virtually the same chemistry before and after processing. By grinding them up and remelting, the materials can usually be reused, with or without mixing them with virgin materials, although a portion of some properties of the material may be lost during the original processing and again during reprocessing. Thermoplastics comprise the majority of all plastics: PS, Nylon, PE, PP, PVC, PC, PET, and most of the "engineering" plastics.

2 Plastics Processing

There are several methods of processing plastics, all of which vary according to the required end products. Some methods can be used for either thermosets or thermoplastics; some can be used only for one or the other. The choice of which material to use is usually based on the expected physical properties of the end product, while the choice of which method to use can be influenced to some extent by the available equipment and the background of the manufacturer. For example, a preform for a bottle can be molded, or it can be produced from an extruded pipe, with some "afterwork" to close the end and form the thread.

To limit the range covered herein, we will not describe processes such as casting (rods or plates), machining, extruding, spraying, rotational or electrostatic molding, or the various methods of sheet molding, lay-up molding, etc., but it is important to be aware of all these different methods used in the plastics industry. Also not covered herein are foam molding or reaction injection molding (RIM), which in principle are not much different from plain injection molding, with the exception that some chemical reactions of the plastic, to impart it some very special properties, take place during the molding operation by combining chemicals just before or during the injection.

2.1 General Considerations in Plastics Processing

The following facts are presented simply, without mathematics, and should give the reader a basic understanding of plastics processing:

Viscosity: a measure of fluidity of the plastic (how fast and how much it will spread when squeezed); it depends on the temperature of the plastic. The warmer the plastic, the lower the viscosity (i.e., the more it will yield) and vice versa.

Temperature: a measurement describing a physical state (hot or cold) of the plastic. (Expressed in °F or °C.)

Heat: a form of energy used to change the temperature. (Expressed in calories or BTUs; it can be changed into equivalent measures of energy, such as kW (electrical) or hp (mechanical).

Heat Conductivity: a measure of the speed with which heat travels through a material. Plastics have generally poor conductivity, which means that heat applied to a plastic from the outside travels very slowly away from the area where the heat is applied. Unless the plastic is moving and mixing while heat is applied locally, overheated spots may develop while other parts are not heated enough for processing.

Amorphous: having a random molecular structure of the plastic (i.e., PS, PC, and PVC).

Crystalline: having a regular molecular pattern, typical for each material (i.e., the "crystals" in PE, PP, Nylon, and PET).

No plastic is fully crystalline, as is ice or table salt. "Crystalline" when used in connection with plastics means only that there is a significant quantity of molecular regions joined in repetitive, regular patterns that exist within an amorphous matrix. One speaks of "percentage of crystallinity" when describing the ratio of the two types of structure within the same piece of plastic.

Crystalline regions disappear upon sufficient heating; at injection temperatures, all plastics are amorphous. As the plastic cools down, the crystalline regions reform, unless some special measures are taken (as in the case of PET for bottles) wherein the transition from hot to cold is speeded up to such extent (by rapid cooling) that the crystals have no time to form. Visually, amorphous plastics are clear (transparent), and crystalline plastics are opaque (translucent).

Figure 2.1 shows schematically the relationship between time during which heat (energy) is introduced into the plastic and temperature.

In amorphous plastics, the temperature rises in a straight-line (linear) relationship to the heat being applied (Fig. 2.1a). In crystalline plastics, after a

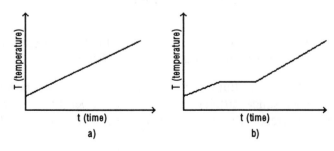

Figure 2.1   Relationship between time and temperature in the heating of plastics for a) amorpous material and b) crystalline material.

certain time, all of the heat introduced into the plastic is used to melt the crystals (crystalline heat) without raising the temperature of the melt. Only when all of the crystals are melted does the temperature of the melt, which is now amorphous throughout, rise again (Fig. 2.1b). Note that during cooling of such a melt, the same "break" is experienced—namely, a time in which the temperature does not decrease until all of the crystals are reformed. During this time, all of the crystalline heat is given up into the cooling medium or the surrounding air.

This knowledge is of particular interest to anyone exposed to purging of injection machines or extruders. A purged "blob" of hot amorphous material, such as PS, cools down fairly fast and evenly; a similar blob of crystalline material, however, such as PE, stays hot (and dangerous to the touch) long after the purging is dropped. This also explains why more heat (and power) is required to plasticize a mass of crystalline material than a similar mass of an amorphous plastic; conversely, it takes more cooling energy to cool a mass of crystalline plastic.

What we have learned above leads us to another pair of graphs (Fig. 2.2), which show another typical behavior of plastics in processing. Exact curves for each material are available from the materials suppliers.

All thermoplastic materials respond to heating according to a characteristic curve (shown schematically) which shows the temperatures and the related times of exposure to these temperatures before the plastic starts to degrade, thereby losing essential properties. Typically, such a curve is a hyperbola; at zero time, the temperature can be infinitely high; at low temperature, the time can be infinitely long (Fig. 2.2a).

For thermosets, the two curves shown have a different meaning. To the left of and below the first curve, no curing takes place. To the right of and above the

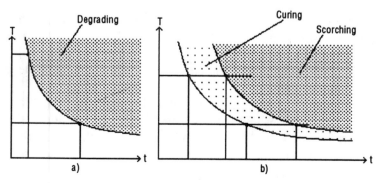

Figure 2.2   Characteristic curves for temperature and related exposure times of a) thermoplastics and b) thermosets.

second curve, the thermoset is overcured and degrades, or "scorches". The area between the two curves defines the region within which curing must be effected. Curing starts at the left curve and should be finished before the right curve is reached; the part must be ejected no later than at this time to prevent scorching. It is easily seen that a higher molding temperature could reduce the molding cycle, but the risk of scorching becomes greater. At lower temperatures, the curing starts later, but there is also more time available before scorching occurs. Preheating of the thermosets takes place preferably in the area to the left of the first curve, and it seems desirable to preheat to a temperature as close as possible to the first curve to reduce the curing time in the mold to a minimum. However, the preheating must be even throughout the mass and must not be too high, to impart the plastic a degree of viscosity sufficient to allow it to flow and fill the cavity completely during compression or transfer. If the material is preheated too much, it will cure before the cavity is filled and produce scrap.

2.2 Compression Molding

A premeasured molding material is placed into the open mold. By closing the mold and compressing the material, the desired shape is achieved. Both thermosets and thermoplastics can be compression molded. The process is used mostly for thermosets, and also for thermoplastics containing very large amounts of fillers, which reduce the moldability (flowability) required for injection molding (i.e., phenolics with up to 60% mineral fillers, for insulators; polysulfones with up to 80% ceramic fillers, for engineering uses). There are three types of compression molding: semi-positive, positive, and flash molding (Fig. 2.3). Flashing is necessary in all types to allow the air or gases to escape.

For thermosets, the raw material can be cold, but it is more often preheated close to the "setting" temperature. The mold is heated with steam or electric heaters, and it stays closed until the product is cured or "set". The hot product is then ejected. Typical products include tires, components for the electrical industry, and dinnerware.

For thermoplastics, the hot (melted) material is placed into the relatively cold mold; the mold then closes and compresses the material into the desired shape. When the part has sufficiently cooled to be handled without deformation, it is ejected. Typical parts so produced include audio records, etc. See also Injection-Compression Molding (p. 24).

For both thermoset and thermoplastic materials processed by compression molding, the mold is open while the material is loaded. During the closing of the

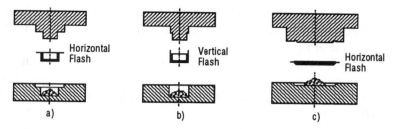

Figure 2.3   Three basic types of compression molds (ejectors and heating/cooling not shown): a) semipositive mold (mostly used), b) positive mold (rare), and c) flash mold (plates, records).

mold, it is unavoidable and sometimes even desirable for some of the material to escape at the parting line, creating "flash". It is, therefore, necessary to provide an excess of material with every shot, which is wasted, or "scrap" with thermosets but which can be reused with thermoplastics. In either case, the flash must be removed to provide a finished product, either by tumbling (if permitted), manually, or mechanically (typically, edge-turning of audio records).

2.3   Transfer Molding

This type of molding is an improvement of compression molding and a forerunner of the injection molding technology. In transfer molding, the mold cavity is closed (clamped) and connected at a "gate" via a "runner" to a transfer "pot". The material is loaded into the pot, and a plunger drives the material into the cavity. There is no flash on the part, but the runners and a certain amount of scrap, or "cull", remaining in the bottom of the pot must be removed before the next shot. This method is used almost exclusively for thermosets, requiring the pot to be heated. Also, to reduce the molding time, the material charged into the pot should be preheated as close as possible to its curing temperature.

For ease of handling, the powdery molding material for phenolics and ureas is usually pressed cold into pellets (each one, or sometimes more than one, representing the product or shot weight). The weight of these pellets can be closely controlled during pelleting, or "tableting". They are then loaded, cold or preheated, by hand or mechanically into each mold cavity or into the shooting pot. Preheating is done either in electric or steam ovens or in microwave ovens.

Because of the loading method, it is more practical to utilize gravity for both compression and transfer molding, that is, to keep the mold parting line horizontal and use a vertical clamping arrangement. In some machines, the lower platen is fixed and the upper platen moves up and down; in others, the upper platen is fixed and the lower platen is movable. These differences in machine design have no bearing on the molding process itself.

The plunger is usually driven by a separate hydraulic cylinder mounted on the platen. In both examples shown (Fig. 2.4), it is possible to move either the lower or the upper platen, but, usually, the platen with the transfer plunger is not moving. With a bottom-mounted plunger, the material is loaded into the pot while the mold is open. After the mold is closed, the plunger rises to push the plastic into the cavities. With a top-mounted plunger, the mold closes first, the plastic is loaded into the pot, and the plunger descends to push the plastic into the cavities. (Note the similarity to injection molding.)

As a variation, there is another method, not further described or illustrated, which is similar to that in Fig. 2.4, but instead of feeding the material into the shooting pot from the top (as illustrated), the plastic is extruded into the shooting pot sideways through a hole in its wall from an extruder below the platen, as indicated by the arrow "EX". Of course, the plunger must stroke below the opening to pick up the charge.

The transfer method is actually the same as the two-stage injection molding system. Practically any injection pressure and shot volume can be achieved by varying the diameter of the plunger. A smaller plunger results in higher pressure but smaller volume, and vice versa. Of course, the shot volume also depends on the stroke of the plunger.

At first, operators were needed to load the raw material and to unload the molded articles. During the curing time, they removed the flash from the parts while attending one, two, or more machines. Later, automation was introduced

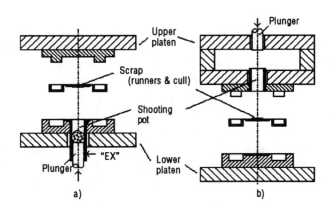

Figure 2.4   Transfer molds (ejectors and heating not shown): a) bottom-mounted plunger; b) top-mounted plunger.

to both load and unload these machines. At about the same time, the use of thermoplastic materials increased dramatically, and the processing of thermoplastics was taken over by the "plunger" machines, which were the forerunners of the present day injection molding machines.

2.4   Plunger (Injection) Molding

Plunger machines are an evolution of the transfer molding machines applied specifically to thermoplastics. The raw material, usually in the form of small pellets, is fed from the top into the side of a usually horizontal heated cylinder. The cylinder is connected via a nozzle, a sprue, and some runners to the mold cavity (Fig. 2.5).

After the mold closes, the carriage with the injection unit advances so that the nozzle contacts the mold sprue bushing. The plunger sliding inside the shooting pot first shuts off the entry port of the raw material and then pushes and compresses the plastic through sometimes fairly elaborate channels in the torpedo near the exit end of the shooting pot. The intent is to expose the plastic to as much heated surface as possible and to melt the granules within a reasonable time period. As the plunger continues to advance, the now viscous plastic is injected into the mold cavity. The pushing force is normally generated by hydraulic cylinders.

The plunger injection system was first used on the original vertical machines by injecting the plastic into a sprue in the parting line of the mold. For practical reasons, however, more and more horizontal machines soon came into use with the mold mounted so that the parting line was in a vertical plane. The main advantage of this change was that the mold cavity could be filled from the

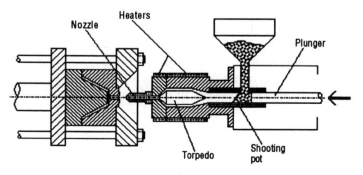

Figure 2.5   Plunger injection molding machine.

horizontal plunger at the center of the part rather than from the edge, which made it practical to mold large items, such as pails, of good quality. The horizontal plunger permitted the type of mold layouts we are familiar with today which are mainly based on the plastic being brought in at the centerline of the machine. Another advantage of this change was that the ejected parts could fall unassisted into chutes or onto conveyors. Operators were needed only where parts could not be dropped without being damaged or where automatic unloading and runner removal was not practical. Mechanical unloading devices, which were, and still are, quite common with thermosets, were not used at first; they made a comeback on horizontal injection molding machines only within the last 15 years.

While the plunger system is fairly simple, even with all the special, sophisticated heating cylinders and torpedoes designed in the final days of the plunger machine to improve and control the melt quality (homogeneity, temperature), the hourly throughput was far too low.

There was a short-lived attempt to increase the output of the plunger system by mounting one or even two large plunger systems on top or at the sides of a machine's main plunger system, which was then used solely as an injection plunger. (Compare with transfer molding, above, and preplasticizing, described below). These systems were very unwieldy and disappeared again after a few years. A good description of plunger molding machines, including two-stage plunger molding machines, can be found in I.V. Rubin's book on injection molding (1972).

One of the main disadvantages of the plunger systems was the inherent inaccuracy of the shot size, a characteristic which depended on the material flowing freely into the shooting pot. Automatic weigh feeding of material into the shooting pot became quite common. It worked very well with larger parts but was not practical with small shots and with fast-running machines.

One application in which the plunger method is superior to the present day screw machines is when it is not desirable to produce a good, homogeneous melt before injecting, as when molding parts with pearlescent or marbleizing effects (i.e., combs, buttons, brush handles, etc.) that are created by mixing two or more materials or colors and injecting the melt while the plastic is not well mixed or melted, as it would be within an extruder.

Marbleizing can be done on screw machines, but special attachments and controls must be added to the extruder. It is simpler to mold these parts using the plunger machine.

2.5 Extrusion of Plastics

In a typical extruder (Fig. 2.6), the material is fed from a hopper into the side of a long, heated cylinder, or barrel, near its end. A specially shaped screw rotates inside the barrel. The screw is driven by an electric or hydraulic motor, often over a reducing gear train or belt drive, and transports the material (in the form of granules or powder) toward the other end of the cylinder. The screw flights are shaped so that the material is forced against the heated inside wall as the screw rotates. Figure 2.7 shows a simplified schematic of plastic in one screw flight.

The material melts gradually as it travels the length of the barrel due to the forced contact with the barrel wall and, most importantly, due to the heat generated by friction between the contacting surfaces of the screw and the barrel, and by friction between the plastic particles themselves. By the time it reaches the end of the barrel, all of the material should be melted (i.e., fluid enough to

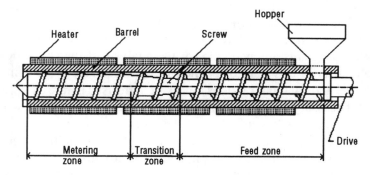

Figure 2.6   Typical plasticizing screw extruder showing zone locations.

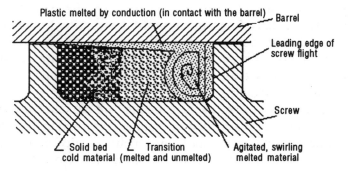

Figure 2.7   Melting of plastic within one screw flight.

be injected into the mold). The material is now said to be plasticized or plasticated.

As indicated in Fig. 2.6, the typical screw consists of three zones. In the first, the feed zone, the plastic particles are conveyed away from the hopper and fed into the heated barrel. The corresponding section of the screw acts like an auger and is designed to be an efficient conveyor.

In the next zone, the transition or compression zone, the particles are melted and the melt homogenized, completing a process which started at the end of the feed zone. This section of the screw differs from the feed section in that it is designed to enhance the friction and contact with the barrel.

Finally, the third zone, called the metering zone, contains a screw section designed to act efficiently as a pump by generating pressure in the now homogeneously molten mass of plastic and to meter accurately by supplying under pressure a quantity of molten plastic that is consistent for each and every second of operation.

The design of the screw flights in the three zones, the length-to-diameter ratio (L/D) of the barrel, and the forces required for the screw drive are now part of a vast field of screw technology. Many different extruder and screw designs exist, many books and articles have been written about this technology, a number of computer programs are available for the analysis of the screw design, and many specialists in this field offer their design services. Most common L/D ratios are 20:1 and 24:1, but ratios as low as 12:1 are used in rare cases, and ratios of 30:1 are necessary for some materials. The screw manufacturer will suggest the proper ratio for each material and for a required throughput.

Compression ratio is the ratio of the height of the flight in the feed zone to the height of the flight in the metering zone. Usually, this ratio is 2.5:1 to 4:1, depending on the plastic. Exact data are available from the materials suppliers.

In the extrusion process, as opposed to the use of extruders for injection molding, the forward pressure generated by the screw is sufficient to drive the melted plastic through an extrusion die, which imparts to the plastic the desired shape, such as sheets, flats, films, tubes, profiles, etc. After leaving the die, the shaped plastic is cooled in special equipment and then cut to length. Wire may be fed through the extrusion die to acquire layers of insulation, as in electrical cables. We will consider only the areas of extrusion technology which are significant to injection molding.

The main advantages of "screw plasticizing" are the relatively large quantities of plastic that can be plasticized per hour as compared to that produced by plunger equipment of similar size, the homogeneity (quality) of the melt, and the relative ease of proper temperature control of the melt. Note that a good melt must have a uniform temperature throughout, with no unmelted granules, or "unmelts", and no overheated, scorched, or burned plastic within the melt, to assure a uniform quality of the end product, whether extruded or molded.

2.6   Thermoforming

The subject of thermoforming is introduced here because of its connection to extrusion and because it can compete with injection molding of disposable containers. The process is similar to drawing of metal containers. An extruded sheet of plastic, supplied either directly from an extruder or from rolls, is heated on the approach to the cavities and then shaped (in multicavity molds) within the mold cavities by punches, by vacuum, or by a combination of both. After forming, the parts are trimmed from the sheet and stacked. The scrap can then be reprocessed.

Thermoforming can be highly productive and often competes with injection molding. For example, some 40,000 drinking cups per machine hour can be thermoformed at about one-half the weight of a molded cup. In such cases, the competing injection molded product must have some functional or aesthetic advantages that outweigh the low cost of the drawn part, such as clarity, stiffness, temperature resistance, etc.

2.7   Injection Molding (with Screw Plasticizing)

Plunger injection molding was described earlier as one alternative of injection molding. Today's injection molding relies almost without exception on plasticizing by means of a screw, so much so that the term "injection molding" by itself means the use of a screw plasticizer. The reasons for this were the tremendous advantages achieved when the screws were introduced in the 1950s:

Throughput: Compared to plunger equipment of similar size, the screw provides much larger quantities of molten plastic.

Homogeneity: Uniformity of the melt is improved beyond comparison. To obtain equally uniform melt temperatures reliably, the plunger machine requires much more time and, even then, lags behind in quality.

Melt quality: The typical frequent defects of plunger molding—melt temperature variations from shot to shot and inclusion of residual near-solid granules, or unmelts—all disappeared with the advent of the screw. Likewise, overheated, scorched, or burned inclusions, frequently encountered in plunger molding, disappeared.

Product quality: Due to the reliability and consistency of the temperature and delivery control available for screws, product quality improved significantly.

Energy: Extrusion plasticizing is more energy efficient than plunger plasticizing. In the latter, plastic is heated largely by conduction from the walls of the torpedo and also, to a moderate degree, by compression due to the plunger. In extrusion, heating is generated by conduction from the barrel, which is greatly enhanced by internal friction between the particles of plastic and between the particles and the screw/barrel combination. This friction is often sufficient to dispense with most of the external heating of the barrel.

Theoretically, the same amount of energy is needed to convert a given amount of plastic from solid to molten, regardless of the equipment used. As a practical matter, what counts is how efficiently that energy is conveyed to the material (i.e., how much of it is lost due to the system design). Extrusion plasticizing, in addition to being more controllable, is more energy efficient than plunger molding.

2.8 Screw Preplasticizing Machines

Screw plasticizers are used either with stationary screws or reciprocating screws. The stationary screw serves purely to plasticize and to feed the melt into a shooting pot that is served by a plunger. The reciprocating screw combines the functions of the stationary screw and the plunger by moving axially as well as rotating, thereby acting as its own plunger after plasticizing the desired quantity of plastic.

This was the earliest "marriage" of plunger and extruder technologies. Plunger machines were modified to relegate plasticizing to an extruder, or preplasticizer, usually mounted above the injection pot, which was then used just as a shooting pot. The extruder, under relatively low pressure, feeds the melted plastic into the shooting pot, from which it is then injected under high pressure into the mold. Many plunger machines were so modified during the late 1950s and early 1960s.

The continuously rotating screw was an important feature in the evolution of screw plasticizing. While single-stage machines must stop the screw during injection, with the two-stage injection systems the screw can rotate 100% of the cycle time. This is made possible by the accumulation of melted plastic in front of the screw while gradually retracting the screw against controlled back

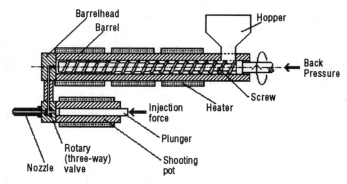

Figure 2.8   Continuously rotating screw plasticizer with rotary three-way valve.

pressure. As soon as the injection is completed and the pressure removed from the shooting pot, the plastic is transferred from the front of the screw into the shooting pot by the force of the back pressure. Increasing the back pressure during transfer provides quicker transfer. The screw keeps rotating and melting the plastic until the molding sequence starts the next injection. A rotary three-way valve (Fig. 2.8) or a check valve prevents the plastic from entering the screw barrel under injection pressure.

While the controls for this system are somewhat more elaborate than for screw injection molding machines, the advantages are spectacular. Because the screw can rotate and plasticize during the entire cycle, the shot size can be much larger than with a screw that stops at every cycle; therefore, a relatively smaller screw and drive can be used. Also, because the screw rotates continuously, the melt quality is more uniform than with a start-stop system. Another advantage of the shooting pot system is accurate control of the shot size. In the two-stage system, the shot volume can be controlled by an adjustable mechanical stop for the plunger, so the amount of plastic injected is very accurately controlled.

Shot size (volume) control is all-important. Obviously, if the shot is too small, the mold will be only partly filled, resulting in scrap. To avoid such short shots, it has become common in the industry to work with an oversized shot volume, thereby creating a cushion of material ahead of the injection piston. As a result, there is more plastic in the space between the plunger and the nozzle than can enter into the mold, so the plunger never bottoms out in the shooting pot when injecting. This means that plastic is under pressure in the mold until the injection force is removed from the plunger. This can create two possible problems:

1. If the clamp force is marginal, that is, if it is barely sufficient to hold the mold shut during injection against the pressure of the plastic, then

in some applications where the surface definition of the product is not important, the shot volume can be adjusted to be without a cushion. The plastic injected is then just enough to fill the cavity space without exerting any appreciable pressure inside the cavity space which could cause the mold halves to separate at the parting line and create flash on the product. This is called "starve-feeding". If the clamp force is sufficient with regard to the mold size and injection pressure, the mold will stay closed and a cushion will not be harmful.

2.   When molding a deep, thin-walled part with little draft per side, the plastic injected with a cushion is easily overpacked and acts like a wedge when cooled. Unless the clamp has a relatively strong mold-open force, it will not be able to separate the two mold halves and create downtime. In such cases, starve-feeding may be a solution to the problem.

2.9   Reciprocating Screw Injection Machines

The reciprocating screw machines were introduced at about the same time as the screw preplasticizer, in the middle 1950s in Europe and in the early 1960s in America. At first, they were considered a temporary fad likely to disappear again soon; by the mid-1960s, there were hardly any plunger machines left. The principle is quite simple (see Fig. 2.9). In an injection molding machine, an extruder is mounted in line with the center of the machine instead of a plunger. It may be mounted at right angles to the center (in vertical or in rotary machines) or, very rarely, even in a vertical position.

The extruder exerts relatively little pressure on the plastic—enough to extrude or to preplasticize, but far too low for injection molding. To overcome

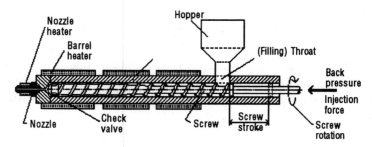

Figure 2.9   Reciprocating screw injection machine.

this problem, the screw is built not only to rotate but also to reciprocate within the barrel, like a plunger. In operation, the screw is allowed to slide backwards within the barrel against low back pressure exerted by a hydraulic cylinder. The amount of plastic to be injected is measured by the length of the backward travel, or stroke, of the screw.

To inject material, the low back pressure is increased to high pressure. The screw is thereby driven forward, and the plastic is injected. To prevent the melted plastic from flowing back into the screw flights, a check valve is usually placed at the tip of the screw or the screw tip is so designed that only a relatively small amount can flow back during injection. The majority of all injection molding machines built today are based on this principle and are called in-line, single-stage, ram-screw, reciprocating screw, "recipro-screw", or simply RS machines. They are fairly simple to control and to operate, and they require less hardware and controls than the two-stage machines.

From a processing standpoint, the RS machines present a reduced risk of material degradation compared to two-stage machines. This is especially important with heat-sensitive materials, such as rigid PVC, which must be injected into the mold in a path without any "dead" corners where the material could stagnate, or hang up, and start degrading because it is not "washed out" with every shot, thus remaining at high temperatures longer than permissible, as has been pointed out in Fig. 2.2a on page 9. However, many other heat-sensitive materials, such as Nylon, Delrin, and PET, have been very successfully molded in a two-stage system, provided the heat controls are reliable and the flow pattern of the plastic is properly designed within the system.

In-line machines are the most common in the industry, mainly because of their simplicity and some small cost advantage. The two-stage setup is used only where the amount of plastic processed per hour is so large that a reasonable economic choice between a much larger single-stage or a smaller two-stage injection unit favors the latter. The accuracy of shot size control with in-line machines is today much better than 10–15 years ago and, with new designs of screw check valves and better electric and hydraulic controls, is rarely a deciding factor in the choice of either of these systems.

2.10   Screw Check Valves and Screw Tips

2.10.1   Ring Check Valve

A ring check valve is shown in Fig. 2.10. As the screw rotates, plastic melts and flows toward the tip of the screw, where it accumulates and pushes the screw

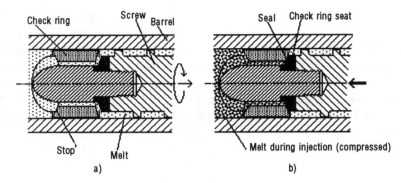

Figure 2.10   Ring check valve a) as the screw rotates and retracts and b) as the screw injects.

back against controlled back pressure. As it pushes so, the check ring sticks to the inside wall of the barrel and is dragged along by a stop, usually consisting of four to six points in a starlike arrangement around the circumference of the screw tip. Unfortunately, as the ring is dragged while the screw is turning, the stops gradually wear down until they fail to retain the ring and must then be replaced. Otherwise, this type of check valve is very good; the flow path is smooth with few hang-ups.

2.10.2   Ball Check Valve

This design (Fig. 2.11) works the same as a ball check valve in a hydraulic system. While the screw rotates and melts the plastic, the ball seats on projections around the flow opening, acting as a stop, and lets the plastic flow through. In a simpler alternative (not shown), the ball is retained by a dowel pin at a right angle to the flow path. During injection, the ball moves against the sealing surface and prevents plastic from reentering the screw flights. This system is as good as the ring check valve and less prone to wear. Sometimes, a bullet-shaped valve element is used instead of a ball, presenting the same ring area to the seal at all times; the ball is free to turn and can create leaks through a worn area of the ring.

The ball check valve presents problems when used with high-temperature plastics. Due to the distance of the flow path inside the tip from the barrel heater, it can be difficult to restart a screw filled with such plastics, and the check ball remains "frozen" and prevents the screw from filling the other side of the check valve.

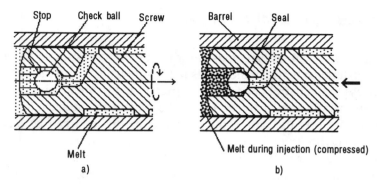

Figure 2.11   Ball check valve as a) the screw roates and retracts and b) as the screw injects.

2.10.3   Plain Screw Tip

The plain screw tip is used almost exclusively with very viscous materials, such as rigid PVC. The melted plastic flows through the narrow gap between the tip and the barrel wall during plasticizing, while the screw turns and retracts (Fig. 2.12). When injecting, the plastic is pushed forward relatively fast so that the amount flowing back through the gap is small compared to the shot size. Therefore, the shot size control depends largely on the cross section and length of the gap and on the repetitive accuracy of the injection speed, the heat controls, the screw velocity, and the back pressure, all of which influence the viscosity. Obviously, if the viscosity is too low, much material will flow back instead of into the mold.

The main advantages of this tip are its almost perfect streamlining, total lack of hang-ups, and no need for maintenance.

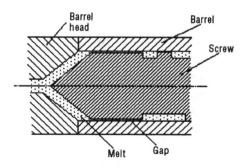

Figure 2.12   Plain screw or "smear" tip.

2.11   Screw Injection of Thermosets

Screw injection machines can be used for both thermoplastics and thermosets. The basic difference between the two is in the screw design, in the construction of and access to the barrel head of the extruder, and in the heating.

With thermoplastics, a freeze-up of the plastic in the barrel is no great problem. By heating the barrel, the plastic is melted and can be pushed out relatively easily; however, in good practice, the barrel should always be emptied before being shut down. With thermosets, it is very important to make sure that no plastic remains in the barrel before shutting the machine down because reheating will *not* remelt the plastic. For this reason, the shape of the screw is such that the cross section of the flights stays constant or even increases toward the point of the screw. Compression ratio of the screw is 1:1 or less. Also, the barrel head must be easy to remove for cleaning.

The heating control for thermosets is more sensitive than for most thermoplastics. The temperature of the plastic should be as close as possible to its optimal curing temperature to get the greatest benefit of the injection molding process. So long as the permissible residence time of the plastic in the extruder is not exceeded—that is, the plastic is injected shortly after it is ready for injection—there is no problem. If it resides too long, even at the desired temperature, it will cure and then be difficult to remove.

The working of the material inside the barrel usually generates more friction heat than is wanted, and this heat must be removed from the barrel. The electric heaters used with barrels for thermosets are for the start-up, but they also contain cooling water channels for the running operation. The mold for thermosets is heated and must be well heat-insulated from the machine platen to prevent heat losses and damaging side effects, such as binding of platens due to heat expansion.

2.12   Injection-Compression Molding

This combination of compression molding and injection molding is used in special applications, such as the pressing of audio records, to acquire the advantages of both systems. Compression molded records appear to have better resolution of the information imprinted than records made by injection molding unless very high injection pressures are used, but, even then, the resolution near the center (point of injection) is better than near the circumference. Also, the center hole of the record is hard to produce due to the necessary use of a center gate.

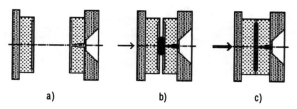

Figure 2.13 Injection-compression molds a) open, b) almost closed as plastic is injected, and c) closed as plastic is compressed.

In the usual method of pressing records, a hot blob of plastic is extruded next to a vertical clamp, mechanically transferred into the open mold, and the clamp closed to press the record (Fig. 3.13). The center hole is then easily and accurately molded by a pin in the lower mold half.

The injection-compression molding process is done in a horizontal machine. The mold closes to within about 3–5 mm of the fully closed position and stops. The extruder then injects a blob into the center of the gap. The mold now closes completely to press the record. The center hole is easily molded by a pin opposite the gate.

It should be noted that other products could also be molded in this way, although at this time the process is almost exclusively used in the record industry.

3 Injection Molding

3.1 Related Technology

Only areas of particular interest to general injection molding will be described here. Injection molds as used for RIM, sandwich molding, foam molding, and other molding techniques will not be described. In general, the term "injection molding" implies the use of relatively high injection pressures, while the aforementioned techniques use rather low pressures. However, it should be understood that many features of the molds for these processes are identical or similar to the molds generally described as injection molds.

3.2 Injection Molds for Thermoplastics and Thermosets

At the center of the molding process is the mold. There is an infinite array of possible shapes of products, but, even for the same product, there can be a wide range of possible mold designs and constructions according to the specific production requirements and the state of sophistication applied to the design of the mold and the method of its manufacture.

NOTE: The purpose of this book is *not* to provide design guidelines but to highlight the various features important in the injection molding technology.

A number of features are common and essential to all molds: mold halves, supply opening (gate), heat exchange, surface finish, venting, and strength. We will examine these features in the following sections.

3.2.1 Mold Halves

Each mold consists essentially of two mold halves which, when clamped together, define the cavity space. This space is the exact negative of the shape of the product to be molded. Removing material from the walls defining the cavity space increases the size of the molded piece, and is fairly easy to do. On the other hand, reducing the size of the molded piece means adding material to the mold wall(s), which can be very difficult. It is, therefore, very important to consider from the beginning where dimensional changes could be required at a later date and to accommodate such changes by certain provisions in the design, such as starting off with a smaller cavity space and enlarging it later.

Usually, one mold half is hollow (female or concave) and forms the outer shape of the part; it is then described as the cavity. The matching half is raised (male or convex) and creates the inner shape of the part; this is called the core. However, the terms "cavity" and "core" can be misleading, for example, when describing the mold for a record disk or for a plastic knife in which cases both mold halves have identical, concave shapes.

The cavity side is usually, but not always, considered to be the side from which the plastic is injected into the mold and is, therefore, often called the "hot side" or the "hot half". It is sometimes called the "stationary half" because it is usually mounted on the stationary platen of the machine. (One notable exception is with stack molds, discussed later, in which the cavities are usually mounted on an intermediary, or floating, platen.)

Usually, a cavity is made of one solid piece; it may include a number of inserts. There must be no projections or undercuts that may prevent the product from pulling out of the cavity when the mold opens. If the product design calls for such undercuts (necks, threads, etc.), the cavity must split to permit the withdrawal, or ejection, of the product. Usually, such a split is through the center of the molded piece; however, it may also be placed through a portion of the piece or just at the spot where the undercut is located by using side cores.

The motion of the splits or the side cores is often tied in with the opening of the mold by the use of cams, levers, or, in cheaper molds, angle pins. Occasionally, side cores are connected to hydraulic core pull cylinders mounted outside of the mold and are controlled independently of the mold motion.

Occasionally, more than two splits are used, but this is rare because of the complexity of the mold construction. A noted example is the "tulip design" wherein four quarter-segments defining the product move with the product during the opening of the mold and spring open to release the product when the segments leave their backing in the cavity block.

It is important to understand that the force generated by the injection pressure of the (viscous) plastic within the cavity tends to spread the cavity open. While in a one-piece construction this force is contained by the strength of the cavity wall, in the case of split cavities this force must be contained by some outside backup features, usually wedges tied to the core side of the mold to lock the mold halves together when the mold closes. Similarly, a side core must be locked to prevent it from moving during injection.

3.2.1.1 Preload

To prevent the mold halves from opening, the wedges must be so dimensioned that, when closed, they apply a locking force, called preload, greater than the expected opening force to prevent separation of the splits and flashing. As the opening force is the product of the injection pressure (within the mold space) and the projected area of the cavity in the direction of the motion of the splits, it is desirable to keep this area of splits (or side cores) as small as possible. A typical example for this is the mold for bottle preforms, in which only the area of the neck ring is split, not the cavity (See Fig. 3.1).

The core side is often called the moving half because it is usually mounted on the moving machine platen; the reason for this is that the ejection mechanism is mostly, but not always, part of the moving platen or is built into the platen as a hydraulic ejection mechanism. Preferably, the product should be stripped from the core side rather than from the cavity side.

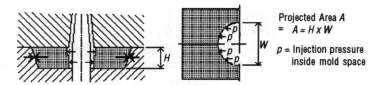

Figure 3.1   Force on slides showing schematic representations of variables.

3.2.2 Gates (Supply Openings)

Gates can be either center gates or edge (side) gates. They are part of cold runner, as well as hot runner, systems.

Sprue gates (Fig. 3.2a) are the first and oldest type of center gates. They were, and occasionally still are, used mainly with very large products, such as pails, which require a substantial amount of plastic. The gate is cut after ejection and leaves a large, unsightly gate mark or vestige. Sprue gates can often be converted to (hot runner) hot sprue gates, which leave hardly any vestige and do not require gate cutting operations.

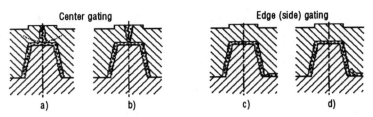

Figure 3.2   Cold runner gates: a) sprue gate, b) pinpoint gate, c) edge gate, and d) tunnel gate.

Pinpoint gates (Fig. 3.2b) are mostly used in 3-plate molds. They provide the nicest looking gate mark and are self-degating. The term "center gate" may appear to imply that the gate is in the center of the product, but this is not absolutely necessary, especially with pinpoint gates, which may be in any convenient location that provides the best flow of the plastic. There may be two or more pinpoint gates in one product.

Edge gating (Fig. 3.2c) is also old technology and still widely used. It leaves usually small gate marks, and, in one variant, the fan gate, the vestige is almost invisible. A fan gate is an edge gate in which the ratio of width to height of the gate is very large. For example, an edge gate may be 1.0 mm wide and 0.6 mm high, while an equivalent fan gate would be 20 mm wide and only 0.12 mm high. The vestige left by the fan gate looks like a fine line.

Tunnel gating is related to edge gating (Fig. 3.2d). The vestige is small and is created as the gate is sheared while the mold opens and the product is dragged past the gate. Depending on the manner of manufacturing, the gate may be round, oval, or rectangular. This method of gating is very widespread.

For many years there was (and is occasionally even today) serious resistance to the use of hot runner systems, which will be discussed later in this book, mainly because of the added costs and because the early hardware was very troublesome in the hands of people not familiar with this method. Also, there was the typical reaction against anything new and unproven. Even today, many molds built in the USA are cold runner molds, but their number is decreasing with improvements in the hot runner technology. Variations on hot runner gates are shown in Fig. 3.3.

3.2.3 Heat Exchange

Heat exchange refers to cooling for thermoplastics and heating for thermosets. Note that an injection mold could function without provision for cooling (in the

a)   b)   c)

Figure 3.3   Hot runner gates: a) open or thermal gate, b) valve gate (VG), and c) hot runner edge gate (HREG).

case of a very simple, experimental mold) by letting the product cool in the mold, where the heat would slowly radiate into the surroundings. However, thermosets require heating to "set" the plastic.

Cooling is done through channels in the mold through which cooling media flow. As a reminder, cooling does not mean that the cooling medium is cold, only that it is colder than the plastic. The medium can be chilled water but also hot water or hot oil. There must always be a temperature difference, ΔT, between the temperature of the injected plastic and the cooling medium to reduce the temperature of the plastic until it becomes rigid enough for ejection from the mold.

Heating of thermosets used to be done with steam. The characteristics of low pressure steam are almost perfect to release, when condensing, the necessary heat at a temperature that is right for many thermosets. The temperature is controlled by regulating the steam pressure. As the pressure can be very accurately regulated, the resultant heat control is accurate and virtually without fluctuations compared to electric on-off controls. However, the temperature range is rather limited if one wants to avoid the use of high-pressure steam boilers and pipes. Most phenolics, ureas, melamines, and rubbers can be and are molded with fairly low-pressure steam heat.

The basic installations for steam heat are large and rather inflexible. The piping is complicated and difficult to keep from leaking, especially in the moving connections (or hoses) to the moving portions of the mold.

Electric heating installation is much simpler. Usually, heating cartridges are inserted where the heat channels would be located on a steam-heated mold. However, cartridges can also easily be inserted in locations where it would be very difficult or impossible to get access with steam channels.

The disadvantage of electric heat is the upkeep of the heaters, the thermocouples, and the controls and, also, the unevenness of temperature distribution within the mold. However, this is of not much concern for practical purposes, and most newer installations use electric heat.

3.2.4 Surface Finish of the Mold

The surface finish of the mold gives the product its desired finished appearance. It is also important to provide an appropriate finish on all surfaces that are more or less in line with the opening of the machine to allow the removal of the product from the mold. Note that the finish does not need to be a high polish so long as the machining marks are in such a direction that they do not create hooks in the product which resist ejection. A certain amount of roughness or even undercuts are sometimes desired to help hold the product on the side from which it is to be ejected.

Polish may even be detrimental to ejection, causing the product to stick to the polished surface, (e.g., when molding PE for lids or containers). In these cases, the surfaces must be roughed with emery paper or with sandblasting to facilitate ejection.

Since a large portion of the mold cost is affected by the amount and type of finishing operations, such as milling, grinding, and polishing, it is very important to establish from the beginning the type of finish required on the molding surfaces and to specify the minimum amount of finish required on each surface. In other words, if milling is good enough for appearance and for release, do not specify grinding or polishing. Similarly, if a grinding finish is satisfactory, do not ask for polish. The amount and quality of polish can be specified based on standards established some years ago by the Society of Plastics Engineers (SPE). Such considerations are very important and can lead to large cost savings, especially with molds for technical articles, whether thermoplastics or thermosets.

3.2.5 Venting

Venting is of special importance for the operation of the mold but unfortunately is very often overlooked or left to the discretion of the moldmaker and added only after mold testing. The reason for venting is easy to understand and is explained below.

As the molding material enters the mold, the air inside the cavity space must escape. When injecting a product from its center (e.g. a cup-shaped article), the air will rush ahead of the incoming plastic toward the rim and try to escape at the parting line. If the injection speed is low and the surfaces mating at the parting line are not sealing, the air can escape. However, such a parting line may result in flashing and create scrap. With higher injection speeds, some of the air may get trapped before it has a chance to escape.

As the air is trapped, it is compressed (Fig. 3.4a) and thereby heated up to a surprisingly high temperature, often high enough to burn the leading edge of the

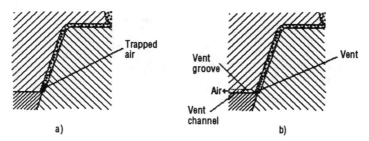

Figure 3.4 Mold space in injection molds: a) unvented mold space and b) vented mold space.

plastic. This can be easily seen as brown or black spots on the molded product. Also, the presence of the compressed air can prevent the plastic from completely filling the mold. In either case, the product may have to be scrapped.

Venting at the parting line is usually fairly simple (Fig.3.4b). The cavity is either surrounded by one or more collector grooves into which the spot vents let the air escape (Fig. 3.5a and 3.6a) or else a continuous vent is provided, surrounding the cavity (Fig. 3.6b). The advantage of a continuous vent is better venting, but this is obtained at the expense of reduced supporting (contact) area between cavity and core (Fig. 3.6), which may lead to crushing of the vent if the clamping force is not properly controlled or if this area is too small.

Figure 3.5b shows a commonly used vent configuration in which each spot vent has its own vent channel leading to the outside of the mold. It is usually machined into the cavity. This method is often used as an afterthought in spots where no vent was provided in designing the mold.

The gap (Fig. 3.5) must be dimensioned so that the air can escape but not the plastic. It usually measures 0.01–0.02 mm, depending on the plastic. The widths

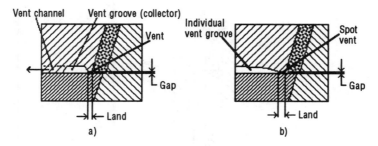

Figure 3.5 Venting is provided at the parting line by a) a collector groove into which air escapes, either through b) spot vents or through a continuous vent (see Fig. 3.6).

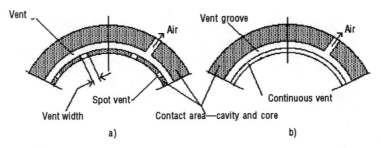

Figure 3.6 Schematic comparisons of a) spot venting and b) continuous venting.

of spot vents vary according to their location, but most common is a width of 5–6 mm. The length of the land is generally 0.6–1.2 mm. The longer the land, the less effective the vent.

In some instances, especially with edge gating but also with center gating, if the injected material can flow faster in some directions than in others due to ribs or large cross sections in the cavity space, plastic streams will join up around the parting line, trapping some air which cannot reach the parting line vents. Ejector pins in the area of such traps will act as vents, called natural vents; otherwise, vent pins (Fig. 3.7) or vents in inserts (Fig. 3.8) at these spots must be provided to ensure trouble-free molding.

Vent design is an important function of the mold engineering and must be considered early in the conception of a mold layout. It is of particular importance with any product with ribs or dead corners, which can trap air. If they are inside the parting line, such vents must be connected to channels that lead the air to the outside. It is also very desirable to make the vents self-cleaning to avoid build-up of residue from the plastic which would eventually block the vent. Parting line vents and ejector pins are considered self-cleaning. If mechanical motion within the vents is not feasible, compressed air should be used at every cycle to blow

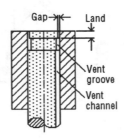

Figure 3.7 Vent pin.

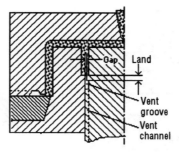

Figure 3.8   Venting in insert.

them clean. If this is not practical, the vent pin must be easily accessible for periodic cleaning.

Vent pins can be either in the cavity or in the core. To avoid witness lines on the molding surfaces, they are usually on the core (i.e., inside the molded product).

In rare instances, the venting is assisted by vacuum. The vent channels are connected to a source of vacuum, which removes the air from the mold space as soon as the mold is closed and before the injection takes place.

3.2.6 Mold Strength

We refer here to the strength required by the mold to resist 1) bursting due to internal (injection) pressure within the mold space and 2) deformation of the mold due to external (clamping) forces. Both are important considerations, even with a cheap experimental mold, if for nothing else but the safety of the operators. No matter what materials are used for the mold (steel, aluminum, zinc, plastic, wood, or other), the construction must be strong enough that the mold will not burst during injection or be crushed when clamped up.

3.2.6.1 Resistance Against Bursting

The required strength to prevent resistance to bursting can be fairly easily figured out by approximating the cavity to a pressure vessel, as shown in Fig. 3.9.

A is the projected area at right angle to the motion of the mold, roughly the height, H, times the diameter, D, of the finished product (Fig. 3.9a).

$$A = HD \tag{3.1}$$

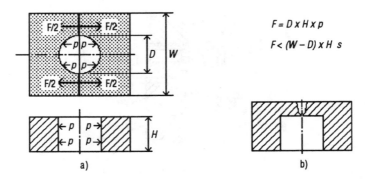

Figure 3.9   Cross sections of mold cavity walls approximated as pressure wells for calculating strength requirements: a) illustrations of variable dimensions, b) one-piece cavity.

Multiplying this area by the (estimated) cavity pressure, p, inside the mold gives the force, F, which the cavity walls must resist.

$$F = Ap \tag{3.2}$$

Note that p is less than the indicated injection pressure on the machine due to pressure losses in the runner systems and in the gate. The cross section, M, of the cavity wall equals the width of the mold, W, less the product diameter, D, times the product height, H.

$$M = (W - D) H \tag{3.3}$$

Strength of the material, s, is expressed in kg/mm^2. From the above, the equation follows:

$$Ap = F < (W - D) Hs \tag{3.4}$$

The mold strength must be sufficient that the cross section of the mold wall will not only be strong enough to withstand bursting but also to overcome any significant elastic, let alone permanent, stretching of the cavity during injection. When using low-strength materials, the walls must therefore be heavier than with higher strength materials. Equation 3.4 ignores the fact that the bottom of the cavity in a one-piece cavity (Fig. 3.9b) adds to the strength of the wall. However, the strength at the open end is relatively low; this must be considered when planning the size and materials for the mold.

3.2.6.2 Resistance Against Clamping

This strength requirement should be quite obvious but is often overlooked. The area at which cavity and core meet when the mold is clamped up must be strong enough to resist crushing and deformation of the mold. If, for some reason, it is not possible to provide sufficient surface at the parting line and not possible or practical to reduce the clamp force, support pillars or blocks must be provided between the two machine platens so that they take some of the locking force and protect the mold from being crushed. This is a simple safety precaution, and every mold should be checked in the light of the above before going it into operation. Failure to do so will result in damaged parting lines and crushed and ineffective vents.

There is usually not much problem with crushing or collapsing of the cores under injection pressure, except with softer materials. Problems may result if the channeling inside the cores is so close to the molding surface that the molding pressure pushes the mold material into the cooling channels.

Up to now, we have considered the six key features common to all molds, regardless of their degree of sophistication. In the following chapters, we will look at the features that are, in a way, optional and at the reasons for their selections.

4 Other Mold Features and Terminology

The following features are essentially dependent on and connected with the actual production requirements of molds: number of cavities, alignment, runner systems, cooling and heating, ejection methods, selection of mold materials, automatic molds, and design, drawings, and standards.

4.1 Number of Cavities

The number of mold cavities depends on two basic considerations: 1) the number of products required per unit of time (hour, week, year) and 2) the size of machine available or designated for the job. Usually, the moldmaker gets an order for a mold with a specified number of cavities and not much additional information except the size of machine the mold must fit. However, additional discussions with the molder will often result in a better choice for the number of cavities, and in better selection of the other parameters listed above, to achieve the optimum size, quality, and price of the mold and the best cost of the molded product.

It is obvious that the best alternatives for the above features are usually the most costly in manufacturing the mold, but such selections can result in greatly reduced molding costs and in lower product costs. On the other hand, it may be wasteful to produce a mold with many or all the costly features if only limited productivity is required or if the product has a limited life before becoming obsolete. There is somewhere a break even point which should be found every time the design for a new mold is being considered as a basis for the decision regarding the number of cavities, etc. The following, oversimplified examples should help to explain these considerations.

Example 1 *A certain product could be molded at a 15-second cycle (one cavity would produce 240 pieces/hour). The annual requirements are 2,400,000 pieces.*

Number of cavities: We assume 5,400 hours/year available per machine based on three shifts of 2,000 hours, or 6,000 hours at 90% efficiency. One cavity would produce $5,400 \times 240 = 1,296,000$ pieces. We therefore need at least two cavities to produce the annual requirements with one mold.

Mold cost: Let us assume that such a two-cavity mold would cost $60,000 and that we plan to write off the mold cost over one or three years.

One-year write-off: $60,000/2,400,000 pieces = $0.0250/piece

Three-year write-off: ($60,000/3)/2,400,000 pieces = $0.0083/piece

Suppose we improve the quality of the mold, by better cooling, better runner systems, etc., at an additional cost of $10,000 but will thereby reduce the molding cycle from 15 to 12 seconds. We now get 600 pieces/hour with a two-cavity mold and need only 4,000 hours to produce the 2,400,000 pieces required. Because of the increased mold cost, the cost per piece changes:

One-year write-off: $70,000/2,400,000 pieces = $0.0292/piece

Three-year write-off: ($70,000/3)/2,400,000 pieces = $0.0097/piece

From this, the mold cost per piece is slightly higher; however, these figures do not account for the cost of the machine time. Assuming the designated machine costs $50.00/hour to run, the total annual machine time cost for this product, with the respective molds, will be:

$60,000 mold: 2,400,000 pieces/(2 × 240 pieces/hour) =
                   5,000 hours × $50/hour = $250,000

$70,000 mold: 2,400,000 pieces/(2 × 300 pieces/hour) =
                   4,000 hours × $50/hour = $200,000

This shows a savings in machine time of $50,000 over one year or $150,000 over three years by choosing the more expensive mold, which is certainly well worth the added mold cost of $10,000.

Machine time cost: This cost will affect the part cost as follows:

$60,000 mold: $250,000/2,400,000 pieces = $0.1042/piece

$70,000 mold: $200,000/2,400,000 pieces = $0.0833/piece

The foregoing considerations for this mold can be summarized in Table 4.1. These figures show clearly the advantage of the more expensive mold, whether for a one-year or a three-year write-off period.

Example 2 *Let us now consider that the annual requirement is 400,000 pieces. Assuming this quantity is required within a short period, we will again specify a two-cavity mold, even though a single-cavity mold would be sufficient for the requirement if spread over a year.*

Table 4.1   **Comparison of Operating Costs for Example 1 Using $60,000 (Cheap) and $70,000 (Expensive) Molds to Produce 2,400,000 Pieces per Annually**

	$60,000 (Cheap) mold		$70,000 (Expensive) mold	
	One-year life	Three-year life	One-year life	Three-year life
Mold cost (¢):	2.50	0.83	2.92	0.97
Machine cost (¢):	10.42	10.42	8.33	8.33
Total cost/piece (¢):	12.92	11.25	11.25	9.30
Total cost/year:	$310,080	$270,000	$270,000	$223,200

Mold cost: Using the same calculations as in Example 1 above, costs are calculated for the cheap $60,000 mold:

One-year write-off: $60,000/400,000 pieces = $0.150/piece

Three-year write-off: ($60,000/3)/400,000 pieces = $0.050/piece

and for the expensive $70,000 mold:

One-year write-off: $70,000/400,000 pieces = $0.175/piece

Three-year write-off: ($70,000/3)/400,000 pieces = $0.058/piece

Machine time cost:

$60,000 mold: 400,000 pieces/(2 × 240 pieces/hour) =
                              833 hours × $50/hour = $41,667

$70,000 mold: 400,000 pieces/(2 × 300 pieces/hour) =
                              667 hours × $50/hour = $33,333

By spending $10,000 more for the mold we save only $8,334 on machine time; this must be carefully considered!

The above new sets of figures are summarized in Table 4.2:

Table 4.2   **Comparison of Operating Costs for Example 2 Using $60,000 (Cheap) and $70,000 (Expensive) Molds to Produce 400,000 Pieces**

	$60,000 (Cheap) mold		$70,000 (Expensive) mold	
	One-year life	Three-year life	One-year life	Three-year life
Mold cost (¢):	15.0	5.0	17.5	5.8
Machine cost (¢):	10.4	10.4	8.5	8.3
Total cost/piece (¢):	25.4	15.4	26.0	14.1
Total cost/year:	$101,680	$61,680	$103,320	$56,640

From the foregoing calculations, it can be seen that a better mold does not necessarily give a lower product cost. When selecting mold features, the molder should take into account how they will affect the mold cost and, eventually, the product cost. If the production run is small or the product life limited, there can often be a good case made for a less expensive mold. With large and practically unlimited production runs, the best quality mold is usually the most advantageous choice.

An infinite number of combinations of features are possible, but decisions on the number of cavities and the selection of the other mold features should be made only after acquiring the best available information regarding required productivity, expected product life, and the machines available or intended for the job to calculate the product cost for several practical alternatives. Note that the true product cost contains much more than the above two components (machine and mold cost), but this will not be discussed here.

We have not considered the cost of the molding material (plastic), which is, in many cases, for each product as large or larger than the cost of the mold per product or the cost of the machine time required to mold the product. The energy cost of cooling (thermoplastics) or heating (thermosets) is roughly directly proportional to the amount of material molded and is not a factor in the above calculations. The size of the heat exchange equipment must be sufficient to accommodate the throughput of molding material per unit of time if it is to provide the required heating or cooling capacity. If this capacity is not available, the molding cycle time may have to be lengthened, and any benefit resulting from an expensive mold may be lost.

4.2 Alignment

This feature refers to the hardware required for matching, or indexing, of cavity and core halves or other mold components that move in the operation of the mold. Several methods used are explained in the following discussion.

In exceptional cases, mold alignment is not required. There are molds in which one side of the "stack" is a flat surface, and misalignment would have no consequences. Also, in rare cases, the alignment provided by the machine platens alone is sufficient to align the mold halves, and no special provisions are required in the mold.

The most common method of alignment is the use of leader pins, usually in combination with leader pin bushings (see Fig. 4.1), although in the case of very low production or experimental molds, the bushing can be omitted. Also, even

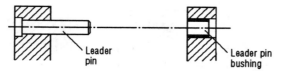

Figure 4.1 Alignment is provided in most molds by leader pins, usually in combination with leader pin bushings.

in high production molds, such bushings may be omitted if space is a problem, provided the plate or other mold component in which the pin slides are hardened and will resist the wear during continuous operation.

Most common is the use of four sets of leader pins and bushings per mold, but quite frequently only two sets are used, either because of cost or because the pins are only used for "near-alignment" (i.e., during mold setup). The final alignment is provided by some of the other methods as described below. There is another reason for the use of leader pins which is not related to alignment, namely, the protection of the cores. This is of special importance whenever the cores are long and thin and could be easily damaged during handling of the mold. The leader pins should be placed on the side of the cores and be just a bit longer than the cores so that the mold can be opened on the bench and rest on the pins rather than on the cores. Also, with the use of automatic parts removal mechanisms, which enter the mold from the side or the top, such leader pins offer a certain amount of protection for the cores in case of malfunction of the take-off, provided they do not interfere with the take-off motion. However, there are exceptions to the rule of placing the leader pins on the core side, notably with 3-plate molds in which the leader pins have the additional function of supporting the floating cavity plate.

The tolerances of the commercially available leader pins and bushings are adequate for many molding jobs. However, especially for thin-walled containers and some technical articles requiring high accuracy of indexing cavity and cores, they are not always satisfactory.

All high-accuracy methods of alignment are based on the wedge principle. These methods can be in the form of two opposing pairs of wedges, at right angle to each other, or in the form of conical wedges. Pairs of wedges (Fig. 4.2) are most commonly used with "technical" molds to bring the two mold halves into alignment by mounting such wedges in the cavity and core retainer plates or, occasionally, they are either part of, or mounted directly onto, the cavity and core blocks.

This ensures very accurate alignment if the final fastening of the core is done after the mold has been clamped up and each block has moved into its proper location. This method is very satisfactory but also quite expensive.

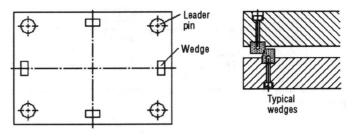

Figure 4.2   Typical layouts of wedges and pins.

Another alignment method is to allow the core block to float a limited amount, even after the final assembly and final tightening of all bolts. This is of special advantage if the centers of the cavity blocks move due to heat expansion. Also, it allows the production of a very accurate mold without excessive and costly tolerances.

Conical wedges come in two distinctly different ways: taper pins and conical fit , or taper lock, between cavity and core. Taper pins (Fig. 4.3) can provide an improvement in accuracy over leader pins. They are usually located in the matching cavity and core retainer plates, in addition to the leader pins. Essentially, the leader pins guide the mold halves fairly accurately into position, and the final location is locked in as the cones of the taper pin and the corresponding taper bushing match up under a slight preload. Accuracy of the location of the taper pins and bushings must be very high to provide the desired effect, and changes are difficult to make.

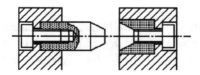

Figure 4.3   Taper pin and bushing.

Occasionally, especially with technical molds, two taper pins are located in each individual stack. The problem in this case is the same as with wedges: the final tightening of bolts holding the core blocks must be done after the mold is clamped up, or the core blocks are mounted so that they can float.

Conical fit of cavity and core, called taper lock, is the most common method used today for the alignment of round cavities or any shape cavity or cluster of cavities which can be fitted within a circle. This method is of special benefit to thin-walled containers for which any eccentricity in the alignment may result in serious core-shift condition. (Experience has shown that an eccentricity of 0.005 mm can create a core shift of 0.05 mm).

Mold components often taper locked for mold alignment are cavity with core, and cavity with core and stripper ring. Fig. 4.4 shows a typical alignment of cavity and core. Note that, in the case shown, the female taper is in the cavity, the male taper in the core; however, it could also be the other way around, usually depending on the method of ejection planned. In some cases, the lip of the female taper may catch the product as it is ejected.

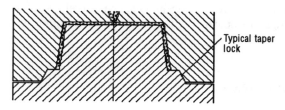

Figure 4.4 Typical taper lock alignment of cavity and core (for simplicity, cooling, venting and ejection are not shown).

4.2.1 Balancing of Lateral Forces in Cavities

The balance of lateral forces in cavities has very serious implications on the alignment of a mold with an offset parting line. In most cases, the "sideways" forces inside the cavity balance each other and do not induce any lateral strain onto the leader pins (Fig. 4.5a).

If however the projected area on one side of the cavity is larger than on the opposing side (Fig. 4.5b), the cavity will want to move away from the core during injection in the direction of the force created by the larger area. If this force is small, it may, in less expensive molds, be taken up by the leader pins, which will eventually lead to excessive wear of the leader pins and bushings and to the loss of dimensional accuracy of the molded product; this is not recom-

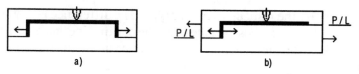

Figure 4.5 Lateral forces in mold cavities a) balanced and b) unbalanced due to offset parting line (P/L).

mended. There are two recommended methods to overcome this problem: 1) use a wedge as part of the cavity/core stack (Fig. 4.6a) or 2) use two cavities opposing each other (Fig. 4.6b).

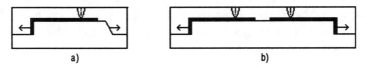

a)   b)

Figure 4.6   Methods for overcoming unbalanced lateral forces are a) balancing the forces using a wedge or b) balancing the forces by using opposing cavity pairs.

4.3   Runner Systems

There are two basically different methods of conducting the molding material from the machine nozzle to the gate where the material enters the mold space: cold runner systems and hot runner systems.

4.3.1   Cold Runner Systems

In a cold runner system, a new runner must be molded at every cycle, which is then ejected together with the products. The runner can be reprocessed and the material used again for molding, usually mixed with virgin material, provided that health regulations or technical (quality) considerations permit adding of regrinds to virgin material.

Cold runners are the earliest method used in plastics molding in all molds for thermoplastics. It is still probably the most common method, especially for molds of low productivity.

There are two basic types of cold runner molds: 2-plate and 3-plate molds. This definition originates with the number of mold plates used in the early days. Today, most molds consist of more than two or three plates, but molds are still called so to identify the respective runner type. The difference is that with the 2-plate mold, the plastic reaches the gate from the parting line and enters the cavity space at the side of the product, but with the 3-plate mold, the runner reaches the gate usually at the bottom, at or near the center of the product.

Note that the sprue gate (Fig. 3.2a) is also a cold runner, as the plastic in the sprue must be cool (rigid) before ejection. It must then be cut from the product.

4.3.1.1 Degating

While the 2-plate system can be self-degating or not (Fig. 3.2c,d), the 3-plate system is inherently self-degating. Figure 4.7 depicts a typical 2-plate, two-cavity mold layout.

The 2-plate mold is a very simple, low-cost arrangement. The leader pins are not shown in the section but would normally be located in the core half (Fig. 4.7). The mass of molding material in the runner system is sometimes very large, especially in the sprue portion. This points to two weaknesses of this system: 1) a slower molding cycle due to the length of time necessary to cool the large sprue and 2) the large mass of plastic to be reprocessed. A combination of hot sprue (see later discussion) and the cold runner eliminates the large, cold sprue at little additional cost.

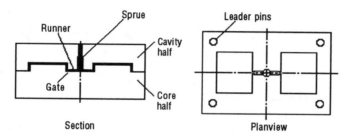

Figure 4.7   A typical 2-plate, two cavity mold layout.

Figure 4.8 shows schematically a 3-plate, two-cavity mold layout in both the mold closed and mold open positions. This shows clearly that the mold has two parting lines.

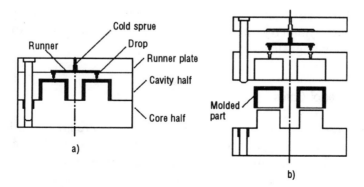

Figure 4.8   A typical 3-plate, two-cavity mold in a) mold closed and b) mold open position.

As the mold opens, the cavity and core half remain together for the first portion of the opening stroke. The pinpoint gate where the "drop" meets the cavity breaks as soon as the cavity plate separates from the runner plate. As the core continues to move away from the cavity, two events take place: 1) cavity and core plate separate, permitting the ejection of the product (mechanism not shown), and 2) the space between the cavity and runner plates permits ejection of the runner, provided the space created is sufficient to permit the runners with the drops on one side and the sprue on the other to clear. Note that runners and products are ejected in different planes, which makes it fairly easy to separate them at the mold.

4.3.1.2 Mold Cost

Understandably, the cost of the 3-plate mold is higher than a 2-plate mold for the same product. However, because of its advantages, the difference is often worth paying for the 3-plate mold.

4.3.1.3 Shape of Molded Product

Two-plate molds are mostly used for rather flat parts but also occasionally for long, slender, tubular products, which are then gated from two opposite sides to prevent core shift. The 3-plate molds can be used practically with any shape of product but are at their best with deep products because they are able to provide center gating for good physical characteristics of the product. The flow pattern within the cavity space during the filling of the mold has a substantial influence on the strength and dimensional stability of the product. With proper center gating, the flow path is uniform around the circumference, especially with parts with rotational symmetry, and practically eliminates danger of core shifting, especially with long, slender cores.

4.3.1.4 Number of Gates

Most molds use only one gate per cavity. However, there are exceptional cases where two or more gates per cavity have advantages. In some 3-plate molds for large parts (e.g., large, nonsymmetrical housings), providing two or more gates at strategic locations may facilitate the filling. In some 2-plate molds, spacing two or more gates evenly around a slender core will prevent one-sided filling and core shift.

4.3.1.5 Mechanisms to Operate 3-Plate Molds

There are a number of mechanisms used for the motion of the cavity plate and for the ejection of the sprue from the runner plate. We will not go into the details of these mechanisms, some of which are tied in with the mold motion, use air or hydraulics, or use a combination of these methods. The earliest 3-plate molds depended on an operator in addition to some mechanism in the mold, and, later on, some external mechanisms were added to ensure that the runner is gone before the mold closes again.

Today, most 3-plate molds operate fully automatically, but, in some cases, some mechanical or electric safety precautions continue to be used to prevent damage to the mold in case the automatic ejection fails to remove a runner. Figure 4.8 shows a cold sprue. However, a hot sprue is better because it eliminates the cold sprue projecting into the runner plate and, thus, simplifies not only the problem of ejection but also reduces the mass of the runner and the time required to cool it for ejection.

4.3.2 Cross Section and Balancing of Runners

The following applies to all types of cold runner molds for all materials. It is very important to make sure that the plastic reaches all gates, whether there is one or more gates for each part, at virtually the same time and under the same pressure.

4.3.2.1 Cross Section

When selecting the cross section of the runners, we are concerned with two opposing requirements. We want the least pressure drop in the flow of plastic from the machine nozzle to the gate; this implies the use of large runner cross sections. (The runner size also depends on the viscosity of the plastic at the molding temperature.) However, we are concerned with the molding cycle time, which is mostly dependent on the cooling time of the mass of plastic in the runners; this implies the use of small cross sections.

The actual selection is, therefore, a compromise based on experience. There are some guidelines regarding size and shape of cross sections, but, even so, runners often have to be increased in size after the first mold tryouts. However, it is always better to start with smaller runners, which can be easily enlarged if necessary.

Figure 4.9 shows a few common shapes of cross sections. Cross section (a) is the best for flow but is costly to match up in two plates. In (b), in which angled

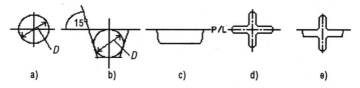

Figure 4.9   Several common runner cross sections.

sides are tangential to the enclosed circle, *D*, is most common. The flow is as good as in (a), but the mass is larger. Cross section (c) is cheap, but the flow is not good, especially if the ratio of width to height is more than 2:1. Cross sections (d) and (e) are sometimes used where the runner must cool fast and be stiff for ejection, especially with very long runners, to prevent hanging up of runners as they fall out of the mold. The pressure drop in these runners is relatively high.

4.3.2.2 Balancing the Runners

The reason for balancing is to ensure that the plastic reaches all gates at the same time and with the same pressure. There is, theoretically, no limit to the number of cavities per mold or to their arrangement within the mold. For practical reasons, however, the number of cavities is usually either a multiple of two, if the pattern is rectangular (preferred for manufacturing reasons), or any number with a circular layout, which has some advantages in the flow since all gates can be at exactly the same distance from the sprue.

Common numbers of cavities in a rectangular layout are 2, 4, 6, 8, 12, 16, 24, 32, 48, 64, 96, and 128. Other numbers are, of course, possible but present some difficulties in balancing (or cannot be balanced) and also in the layout and manufacturing of the cavities and the cross drilling for cooling; they are usually avoided. Some multicavity molds have been built with an odd number when the general layout and the machine capacity suggested such special approach. In these cases, balancing was only approximated, but the flow was even enough for the type of product not to cause any problems. With circular layouts, the most common is 3 cavities, but 5, 10, 12, and others have been successfully built.

In "family molds", two or more different products, sometimes of vastly different size, are produced in one mold, at the same time. The molding cycle of such family molds is governed by the speed of the slowest product (the one requiring the longest cooling time). However, with low-production items, it can be very economical to have one mold with several different products, so long as their required quantities match. This is quite common in the toy industry, where the mold life is rarely more than one year and the quantities are low. Typically, a toy car mold may contain a car body, four wheels, a steering wheel, a driver, two axles, etc. "Geometric" balancing of runners is almost impossible, but, usually, after mold tryout, the size of some runners and gates can be increased to provide optimal molding conditions. This is quite acceptable if the total production is not very high. A disadvantage to consider is that if only one piece is flawed, the whole set is useless because the flawed piece would be missing on assembly.

High-production molds are sometimes family molds if the products are of similar size and have the same molding speed and if there is a definite advantage of molding two matching products at the same time, because they will be assembled immediately downstream from the molding operation. Typical cases are Petri dish bases and covers, CD "jewel box" assemblies, etc. There is also the advantage that in matching products, the color match will be no problem since both (or all) pieces are molded from the same batch of material.

Figure 4.10 shows a few typical layouts of the more common 4-, 6-, 8-, 12, 16- and 24-cavity arrangements. Note that there is theoretically little difference between the balancing for cold, hot, or warm runner molds, and the same patterns apply for all systems. There are, however, variations, which will be pointed out where they occur. The difference is mainly in the method of manufacturing the manifolds. In cold runner molds (2-plate or 3-plate), the runners can be milled; in hot runner molds, they are usually drilled and therefore cannot have curves. Also, hot runners require no venting or cold slug traps.

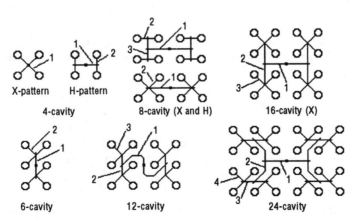

Figure 4.10 Typical layouts of different multicavity mold arrangements (1, 2, and 3 refer to the order in which the material reaches each runner branch in the mold).

4.3.2.2.1 X and H Patterns   The four- and eight-cavity layouts show two typical common arrangements. The selection depends mostly on the general mold layout. The X pattern has somewhat shorter branches but more severe changes of direction and probably more uneven flow in its four branches than the 90° turns of the H pattern. Very often, with a larger number of cavities, the first branches follow the H pattern, and only the last branches are either in H or X, as shown in the 16-cavity layout (Fig. 4.10).

4.3.2.2.2 Cold Slug Traps   These traps are the extensions of each branch beyond the point where the next set of cold runners branches off. The idea is to catch the leading point of the inrushing material, which has cooled off somewhat, and prevent it from blocking or slowing the flow as it continues toward the gates. The usefulness of these traps has lately been questioned, and many molds function without them. It may have been important on older machines with slower injection speeds, where the leading edge of the incoming plastic cools off rapidly.

4.3.2.2.3 Changes in Cross Section   Every time a channel is split into two or more branches, the amount of material and its flow is also divided, and the cross section may be reduced without undue increase of pressure losses. With cold runners, the amount of plastic in the runners is reduced. Remember, more material in the cold runners means less injected plastic is used on products and must be reground (thermoplastics) or scrapped (thermosets). Runners, in fact, reduce the useful injection capacity of the machine. With some small products, the mass of the runners is often more than the mass of all the molded parts together. Also, the more mass in the runners, the slower they will cool.

For hot runners, it is also important to keep the size of the runners to a minimum to keep the "inventory" (material residing in the hot runner manifold) small so that the material is not exposed too long to the heat of the manifold to avoid degradation.

4.3.2.2.4 Balance of Flow   Theory, as well as observation, indicates that whenever the plastic changes flow direction, as at a split, the flow pattern after the split is not exactly half of the flow before the split, which could cause some minor pressure differences at the gates. Generally, the pressure drop at the splits is much less compared to the drop at the gates.

4.3.2.2.5 Changes of Direction of Flow   A difference in the flow is also quite likely to occur if the intersection is at right angles, compared to one at an angle of 45° as shown in some of the diagrams in Fig. 4.10. It is quite likely that plastic flows easier into a runner branching off at 135°, almost in continuation of the original flow, than in one almost doubling back at 45°.

Changes in direction also act to mix up the plastic flowing through the runners. In hot runner molds, with some materials (e.g., bottle grade PET) such changes in direction are introduced deliberately in addition to the split points to better mix the flowing material.

4.3.2.2.6 Individual Balancing of Cavities Should the uneven filling of some of the cavities be serious, it must be corrected by increasing the runner or the gate size until all molded products are equal. This, however, is not very desirable, especially if the mold is so constructed that all the cavities are to be interchangeable. Such individual adjustments will then require identifying the each of the various cavities with its gate size.

4.3.3 Runners for Thermosets

Both cold runner (2-plate and 3-plate) molds are being used with thermosets and thermoplastics, although there are certain differences in mold construction, viscosity of material, and heating and cooling.

4.3.3.1 Mold Construction

The similarity of 2-plate molds for thermoplastics and transfer molding is shown in Fig. 3.4 (p. 33) and in Fig. 4.7 (p. 47). The only difference is that the sprue for thermosets is much larger; in fact, the sprue is the diameter of the shooting pot itself. To save scrap, the shot is sized so that the plunger almost bottoms out and leaves just a thin disk (the cull) to which the runners are joined. In all other respects, the mold can be laid out exactly in any pattern shown in Fig. 4.10.

4.3.3.2 Viscosity

Many thermosets are much more viscous at the molding temperature than thermoplastics and, therefore, need larger cross sections for their runners so as not to cause too much resistance during injection. This is unfortunate because it increases the amount of scrap. The runners selected are often circular (Fig. 4.9a), which gives the largest cross section for best flow, and, at the same time, the least circumference, which reduces the flow resistance. Also, often the 90° turns are avoided by curving the runners when branching off (Fig. 4.11).

Figure 4.11   Runners in this layout are curved to avoid 90° turns in the branching off.

4.3.3.3 Heating and Cooling

The molds for thermosets must be heated to set up the plastic, but for thermoplastics they are cooled. There seems to be a contradiction in terms to call these molds "cold" runners even though they are heated; maybe a term like "stiff runner" would have been more appropriate and would apply to both types of plastics. The "hot runner" could then be called "fluid runner" or some similar name. However, the terms "cold" and "hot" runners are so common in the industry that we will stick to them. We have, however, taken the liberty of calling the equivalent of the hot runner systems (for the thermoplastics) "warm runner" systems in the case of thermosets. Some people call them cold, some hot, and the intention here is to provide a clear distinction in the naming of these various systems. There is no serious technical problem in building 3-plate molds for either thermosets or thermoplastics as long as the above discussed points are observed.

4.3.4 Weld (Knit) Lines and Flow Lines

Weld lines occur wherever two streams of plastic meet inside the cavity space. This may occur when the product is designed so that points within the cavity space can be reached from two directions by the plastic flow. While this occurs usually at a remote point opposite the gate, it can happen at any point. The location of the weld depends on the speed of the plastic flowing through the cavity space. If one flow path is more restricted that the other, the weld will appear nearer the gate on the side of the restricted path. Weld lines also occur at the point where the streams from each gate meet if more than one gate is used. This occurs with any runner system, whether cold, warm, or hot. Typical schematic examples are shown in Fig. 4.12.

The weld or flow lines are largely caused by molding conditions. With thermoplastics, if the melt is too cold, it will not weld or knit properly. The resulting junction is unsightly and, worse, not as strong as the rest of the product and more likely to break under load. To remedy this problem, the injection pressure usually must be increased to make the plastic flow faster, and the melt or coolant temperature usually must be elevated, which affects the molding cycle adversely. In some cases, even these adjustments may not be enough, and the product design may have to be revised to thicken the part at the joint to give it a larger surface for welding. If possible, the cavity should be well vented at the spot where welding is to occur.

Flow lines are similar to weld lines. They are usually caused by the flow of plastic around an obstacle in the flow path, such as a pin. The plastic in the lee of the pin must rejoin, and if the molding conditions are not right, it will leave a flow line (Fig. 4.12).

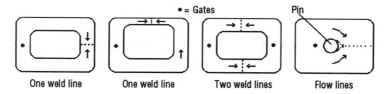

Figure 4.12 Schematic diagrams of weld (knit) lines and flow line.

The above conditions can be experienced with thermosets if the plastic arriving at the joint is already partly set. In this case, the melt or mold temperatures must be lowered, again adding to the cycle time.

4.3.5 Hot Runner (Thermoplastics) and Warm Runner (Thermosets) Systems

The major characteristic of these systems is that the plastic in the runners is kept hot or warm all the way from the machine nozzle to the gate where it enters the cavity space.

"Hot" means roughly the same temperature as that at which the thermoplastic leaves the machine nozzle; depending on the plastic, it is between 130 and 350 °C, or even higher. Generally, the hot runner does not add heat to the plastic; it just maintains it at the level which has been found most suitable for the molding of a specific product. The accuracy of the temperature controls for hot runners is generally not very demanding, except for heat-sensitive materials such as Nylon, PC, PET, etc.

"Warm" also means roughly the same temperature as that of the thermoset material coming from the injection unit, but in this case temperature control is very important. The range between the desired (high) temperature that provides the best molding conditions and the setting temperature of the plastic is very narrow. If the temperature is too low, the molding cycle will be too slow and uneconomical. If the temperature is too high, the plastic will set up in the runners, and the mold portion enclosing the runner must be taken apart to clean out the set plastic. Even if the mold is properly designed to allow easy access to the runner system, this still causes considerable down time. The temperature range for some phenolics is between 100 and 110 °C. Any interruption of the molding cycle increases the time that the warm thermoset is exposed to this temperature; even if the temperature is well controlled, the time factor will make the material set up (Fig. 3.2b, p. 30).

Before going into details of the hot or warm runner molds, one should be aware that every 3-plate mold could be rebuilt into a hot or warm runner mold, molding material permitting. Today, this includes most materials. However, material manufacturers should always be consulted. Also, there must be enough space to accommodate the hot runner nozzle; this is usually the problem with small parts. A 3-plate drop needs much less space than a hot runner drop (nozzle).

4.3.6 Hot Runner Molds

There are two different constructions of hot runners: 1) insulated runner molds and 2) (true) hot runner molds. "Through shooting" is an earlier development of the insulated runner mold as we know it today and is now only rarely used. It depends on the poor heat conductivity of most plastics but is used with relatively few plastics, such as PS, PE, and PP. Through shooting requires fairly fast molding cycles (less than 15 seconds, as a rule) to avoid freezing of the plastic in the sprue.

Figure 4.13 shows how through shooting works. During injection, the sprue fills with plastic. The material closest to the cooled walls will freeze, and,

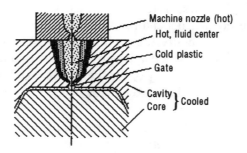

Figure 4.13   Through shooting mold.

because of the good insulation properties of the plastic, the center of the sprue loses very little heat to the surrounding cavity. After injection, the gate freezes, and the product, when stiff, can be ejected while the frozen slug in the gate locks the hot plastic in the sprue. With the next shot, the cold slug in the gate is pushed into the product, where it is melted by the incoming hot plastic. As long as the cycle is not interrupted, shooting can go on forever. If the cycle is interrupted for any length of time sufficient for the hot center to freeze, the whole sprue must be removed before restarting. Through shooting allows the use of very cheap molds and is very efficient. The disadvantage is that it applies only to single-cavity molds and requires a certain amount of skill for start-up.

4.3.6.1 Multicavity Insulated Runner Molds

This development is based on the through shooting method and functions basically in the same manner as explained in connection with Fig. 4.13. The principal difference from the through shooting method is that it can be used with any number of cavities from two up; in practice, it is rarely used with more than eight cavities.

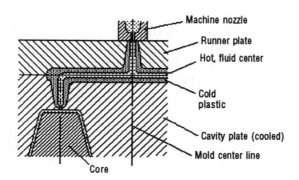

Figure 4.14   Typical insulated (hot) runner mold.

Figure 4.14 shows the essential construction leading from the machine nozzle to a cavity. The most important requirement for these molds is easy access to the runner space between the runner plate and the cavity plate.

While it was simple with the through shooting method to back up the machine nozzle to get access to the frozen sprue slug, with the insulated runner molds, the two plates must be separated to remove a frozen runner. There are several methods for doing this, and we will highlight the important requirements.

1. To assure alignment between cavity and runner plate when closing the runner space, the leader pins should be in the runner plate, or auxiliary pins should be provided.

2. The two plates must be locked together solidly before injecting. Theoretically, the clamping pressure alone is sufficient to prevent plastic from leaking between the two plates; however, it is conceivable that injection may accidentally occur without the mold being clamped (i.e., for purging). The plastic would then escape sideways under high pressure and possibly cause a serious accident.

   Normally, several screws with their heads at the mold parting line (between cavity and core plate) are used for locking the runner and cavity plates together. There are also some lever mechanisms in use to facilitate the opening and locking of the runner space, but they must always be used in conjunction with screws for safety.

3. During start-up, the runners must be filled before the plastic reaches the cavities. The volume of the runners is often considerably larger than the shot size, and it takes two or more injection strokes before all cavities are filled. This is the most critical time of the system operation. If the mold is too cold or the runner system is too large for the injection unit, the runner could (at least in part) freeze before the mold becomes fully operable and must be removed. The start-up process must then be repeated. This can happen several times at every start-up, particularly with molds having a large number of cavities.

4. Safety of setup: Each repeated mold start requires the removal of screws from the parting line, the moving of the cavity plate to get access to the runners, the removal of the runners, and the repositioning of plate and screws—all "rush-rush" to get the mold into operation. These repeated steps are often performed by two operators, one on each side of the machine, which is inherently unsafe; such mold starts should be performed only by a well-qualified team.

5. Number of cavities: With the foregoing safety considerations in mind, it becomes clear that as the number of cavities and the mold size increases, the difficulties in start-up grow exponentially. For this reason alone, the number of cavities seldom exceeds eight, although up to 24-cavity molds have been built and run successfully.

6. Runner size: There is some controversy about the cross section of insulated runners. The thicker the runner, the better it will conserve the heat, but it will also take longer to fill the runner (more injection strokes). The North American industry prefers heavier runners in the area of 16–20 mm Ø. In some European designs, runners of

8–10 mm Ø are common. If the cycle speed is fast (less than 10 seconds), these runners will perform very well. For slower cycles, the larger diameter is necessary in any case.

7. Balancing of runners as shown in Fig. 4.10 is highly recommended. Generally, the same size cross section is used for all runners within a mold; they are not reduced toward the gate.

8. Heat expansion and cooling of runner plates: Generally, there is no need for cooling as there is little heat lost from the plastic into the plates. Heat expansion problems, often associated with hot runner molds, are usually not a factor in this system.

9. Operation: Once the mold has started to produce, it can run practically forever. It is simple, there are no heaters to burn out, and the only problem is the plugging of gates due to dirt in the plastic. Even so, the mold can keep on running with the drop frozen until the next time the mold is cleaned out for start-up.

10. Color changes are easy to effect without stopping the run. The hot, central channel where the plastic flows will be replaced after a few shots with the new color, while the surrounding, cold plastic is unchanged in its original color. This can be easily seen when sectioning a removed runner after a color change.

11. Mold cost: Obviously, molds using this method are fairly inexpensive. Even so, they should be used only where the requirements are high enough to keep the mold running for a long time.

There have been some improvements to the concept of insulated runners to facilitate the start-up. The most important one is the introduction of heaters inside the drop to keep the plastic near the gate hot and to extend the critical time in which freezing could occur, resulting in the need for restarting. Fig. 4.15 shows a typical nozzle heater.

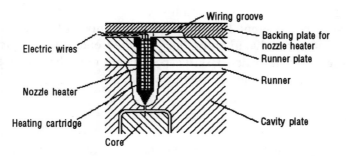

Figure 4.15   Heated nozzle for insulated runner.

This is really a step toward true hot runners, but the start-up, though easier, is still possible only after removal of the old, frozen runner. One of the advantages of the true insulated runner, the absence of troublesome heaters, has been lost. Still, this design made it possible to mold PS, which is a better heat conductor than PE or PP and was very difficult to mold without it using the original insulated runner.

A next step toward true hot runner systems is to position heater cartridges (in tubes) inside the distribution runners leading to the drops and inside the sprue that receives the plastic from the machine nozzle. In this way, it is actually possible to start up a mold without removing the runner. The problem with this system derives from the complexity of the runner plate—which has to contain all the runners that must intersect off-center to provide the proper flow path—in which the tubes with the heaters must be positioned and supported and in which access must be provided for the wires. The temperature of the plastic on its way from the sprue to the gate is also very difficult to control to avoid overheating or cold spots. Also, heating cartridges are not very reliable, especially in a very humid atmosphere, and fail frequently due to shorts across the lead-in wires. Another problem is that in such a crisscrossing of bores, there are corners in which the plastic can hang up and which are difficult to clean.

There is a positive side to this system in that the plastic is heated from the inside and is therefore hot where it contacts the heated tubes but cold on the outside where it touches the mold plates, conducting little heat into the mold. Some of these systems are advertised as hot runners, even though they are really internally heated insulated runner systems.

There are many molders who swear by the true insulated runner molds because of their simplicity and low cost; they don't mind the start-up problems and are obviously not concerned about the safety aspect. Today, there are also some designs available which automate the process of runner removal and the restarting of true insulated runner molds.

However, for safety reasons, it is now preferred to avoid insulated runner molds and to build true hot runner molds, which are easy to start, as reliable to run, and have no inherent limitation of the number of cavities. They are obviously more expensive to build, but with the trend toward more and more automation and the elimination of skilled personnel around the molding machines, they are, at least at this time, the proper way to go.

4.3.6.2 True Hot Runners

The definition of a true hot runner mold is the ability to start up from a cold mold without intervention by an operator, as is required with insulated runner molds.

To achieve this, it must be possible to heat the plastic in the runner system on its way from the machine nozzle to the gates so that, after a preferably short warm-up time, the machine may be started up producing immediately. This does not mean that the parts first ejected from the mold will be perfect; such results can only achieved after the whole system—machine and mold—has thermally stabilized. But it does mean that all cavities function from start-up.

4.3.6.2.1 Hot Sprues Hot runners usually mean molds with two or more cavities. However, the hot sprue is also a true hot runner under the above definition. Therefore, before describing the multicavity hot runners, we will look at these hot sprues.

Figure 4.16 shows schematically the construction of a hot sprue. A multitude of designs is in use, but they all have a duct in common which is electrically heated, either internally or externally, to bring the plastic from the machine nozzle to the gate of a single cavity or to the center point of a runner system, which can be a hot runner distributor or a cold runner as previously described.

Combination hot-cold runner systems do have benefits. When used with a cold runner, the advantage of the hot sprue in a 2-plate mold is that it eliminates the mass of material normally in a cold sprue and thereby reduces the mass of material in the runner system. Also, the hot sprue does not require any added time to cool the plastic in the sprue, as would a cold sprue. A 3-plate mold has the added advantage in that it eliminates the sprue projecting into the runner plate (Fig. 4.8, p. 47), thereby reducing the required opening stroke and facilitating ejection of the runner, making fully automatic ejection of the runner easier.

The combination hot-cold runner is widely used, particularly with multicavity molds that cannot be built as complete hot runner molds because the molded products are too small and there is not enough space to accommodate the hot runner drops. When the hot sprue is used with a hot runner distributor, it is usually part of the construction of the hot runner system and therefore will not be further discussed.

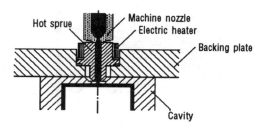

Figure 4.16   Hot sprue (bushing).

4.3.7 Distribution Systems

Discussion of distribution systems and of nozzles, or drops, will be presented separately. Since there are so many different systems and designs, we shall attempt to highlight the features of some of the most frequently used systems and their advantages and disadvantages. Basically, two distribution systems are used: 1) fixed plate and 2) floating plate.

4.3.7.1 Fixed Plate Distribution

The distribution is inside a plate that is part of the mold plate stack (Fig. 4.17). This early method is common in European molds. The runners are bores in a plate or, rarely, milled channels; they are usually arranged in a balanced pattern. The area between the runners is bored out to provide for heating cartridges near the runners and laid out so as to prevent cold spots or overheated areas. The temperature of the plate is usually controlled by a single thermocouple.

The distribution plate is insulated from the backing plate and the cavity plate by a heat-insulating material, such as asbestos-cement or, more recently, asbestos-free products. These insulators must have high compressive strength, preferably not less than half the strength of mild steel, since the whole clamping pressure of the mold is taken up by them. While the thickness of the insulator between the backing plate and the distribution plate may have to be substantial (20 mm or more) for good insulation, the insulation between the cavity plate and the distributor must be thin or else the drops to the cavities will become too long and present heat problems in the gate area.

Another serious problem is presented by the heat expansion of the distributor. The cavity plate must be cold, as must the backing plate, which rests on the machine platen. These two plates do not expand, whereas the heated plate will. This expansion can be significant even in relatively small molds. The linear

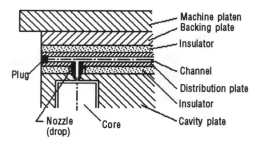

Figure 4.17   Hot runner with a fixed distribution plate.

coefficient of heat expansion for steel is $f \approx 0.0011$ mm per °C per 100 mm length.

Example 3 *At mold temperature T_m of 20 °C and distributor temperature T_d of 220 °C, we have a ΔT of 200 °C.*

The difference of expansion for plates 400 mm long will be:

$$f = 0.0011 \times 4 \times 200 = 0.88 \text{ mm } (0.030 \text{ in.}), \qquad (4.1)$$

a substantial amount. The alignment can therefore be secured only between the cooled cavity and core plates, while the hot runner distributor must be left free to move laterally.

4.3.7.1.1   Cavity Centers   To make up for the differences in center distances of the cavities and the centers of the corresponding nozzles, the designer will anticipate the expected expansion and position the nozzles at closer centers than the cavities so that the centers will be correct at the planned operating temperatures of the plastic and the mold. This is good for one specific combination but does not leave much room for changes in the material and may affect the molding cycle, which will have to be adjusted so that the ΔT between the plates is actually as it was anticipated. Failure to have the centers in line during operation can seriously affect the flow of plastic at the gate, which would then allow easier flow on one side than on the other, possibly causing core shift or uneven filling of the mold.

4.3.7.1.2 Safety   In fixed plates, the channels usually are drilled from the edge and then plugged. This puts the plugs under tremendous strain during injection, since the full injection pressure acts on the inside of the plugs. There have been cases of such plugs coming loose and shooting across the molding room, injuring bystanders. This is not acceptable by any safety standard.

4.3.7.1.3   Hang-Ups and Dead Corners   Cross drilling leaves some unavoidable corners in which the plastic could hang up. This is not satisfactory for the molding of easily degradable materials because traces of the degraded material are washed out by each freshly injected stream and contaminate the molded product. There are some methods for placing inserts in the channels to provide a smooth, self-cleaning flow path. A typical example is shown in Fig. 4.18.

Note that such inserts are also used in other types of distribution systems. The drawing in Fig. 4.18 is only schematic; there are a number of shapes and many methods to keep the insert and plug from loosening, which we will not describe here. Since it is desirable to gain access to the channels for cleaning, welding is not recommended, although it is frequently done.

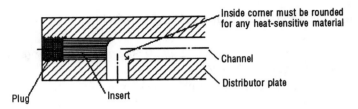

Figure 4.18   Flow-directing insert in channel.

The best safety precaution, even if more expensive, is to completely surround the hot runner distributor with a plate or set the distributor into a recess in the cavity or the backing plate. The plastic can then escape only slowly in case the plug loosens or a crack occurs in the material of the distributor.

4.3.7.2 Floating Plate Distribution

In floating plate systems, the runners are separated from and suspended in the mold plate stack (Fig. 4.19). This method is used today by most North American moldmakers.

The distributor, or manifold, may consist of a plate, a combination of plates, or a combination of tubes and plates. There are numerous designs on the market; we will look at the essential features.

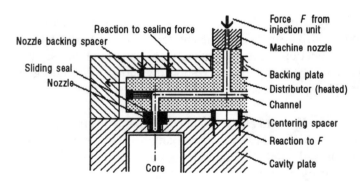

Figure 4.19   Hot runner mold with a floating distribution plate.

One feature common to all of these systems is that the clamping force does not pass through the distribution system but goes around it. The forces affecting the distribution system are only the internal pressures created by the injected plastic and the reaction to the sealing forces at the machine nozzle and at the drops.

Differences in heat expansion are either compensated for by "false" centers, as in the fixed plate distribution systems, or by sliding seals where the drops meet the distributor. Sometimes, a combination of both methods is used.

4.3.7.2.1 Clamping Force Clamping force goes from the backing plate directly to the cavity plate without affecting the hot runner system. Both plates are relatively cold; the cavity plate is cooled (not shown in Fig. 4.19), and the machine platen, the "hot" platen, is also cold and, like the rest of the clamping system, at ambient room temperature.

4.3.7.2.2 Auxiliary Supports Because of the large span over the distributor, the designer must provide support pillars or other methods to prevent deflection of the plates. It is preferable to take up the clamp force near the centers of the cavities, which means that such supports must either pass through the distribution plate, or the cavity plate must be so shaped that the corresponding nest in the backing plate may follow the shape around the manifold. Both methods may be used, either alone or together (Fig. 4.20).

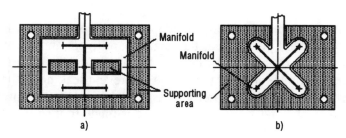

Figure 4.20   Support for the cavity plate a) through and b) around the hot runner manifold.

4.3.7.2.3 Heat Expansion Obviously, the manifold will expand in all directions when heated to operating temperature, but most expansion occurs in a plane at right angles to the machine center line, as indicated by an arrow in Fig. 4.19. The manifold will also expand in the direction of the center line.

Expansion outward from the manifold center is similar to that described for fixed distribution plates. As shown in Fig. 4.19, the center of the manifold is held in the mold center by a spacer sleeve or by a dowel. The spacer sleeve also supports the manifold against the pressure exerted by the machine nozzle, which could be as high as 5–10 tonnes.

The drop (nozzle) is seated in a fixed position in the cavity where the channel in the manifold meets the channel in the nozzle, but there is no fixed connection. This enables the manifold to slide across the nozzle face during the heating-up period. When fully heated, the centers meet to create a smooth transition of the channel bores. Misalignments by as little as 0.1 mm can cause degradation with heat-sensitive materials.

Expansion in line with the mold occurs as the distributor and the nozzle (see later discussion) heat up. Before heating, if the mold is properly dimensioned, there is a slight gap (≈ 0.05 mm) depending on the length of the elements, between the manifold and the nozzle and between the manifold and the nozzle backing spacer, so that no force acts on the manifold in this direction.

As the operating temperature is approached, the gap not only disappears but the manifold is clamped with considerable force between the nozzle and the backing spacer. Sufficient force is exerted to create a seal between the nozzle and the manifold so that no hot plastic can escape, even under high injection pressures. This principle of a sliding seal is very efficient and is used in many hot runner systems.

Caution is necessary. If the dimensions are not correct, the forces generated by the heat expansion can be high enough to break the bolts which hold the backing and cavity plates together. Too much clearance, however, will cause the plastic to leak.

There is another, rarely used method for overcoming the outward heat expansion. A composite manifold is made in which the center of the manifold assembly and the end positions at the nozzles are fixed, and the intervening length is made up by externally heated, telescoping tubes. The machining accuracy and the finish must be very good to prevent leaking at these sliding joints, which have no external forces to assist in the sealing, although in some cases the wall at the ends of the inner tubing is made thin so that the plastic pressure can expand it and thereby create the seal.

4.3.7.2.4 Balancing   As a rule, the designer should attempt to balance the runners. Most hot runner manifolds are balanced, although there are cases where balancing can be only partly achieved if the mold layout is such that a fully balanced layout would make the mold unwieldy or too complicated. In principle, balancing of hot runners is similar to the balancing of cold runners. There are, however, some important differences due to manufacturing requirements. Because all hot runners manifolds are made from solid plates, with drilled channels for the plastic flow, it must be possible to produce the desired pattern with a series of straight bores. If a balanced pattern cannot be achieved in one level, the manifold must be made thicker and two or more levels of holes drilled to produce the desired pattern. A typical arrangement is shown in Fig. 4.21.

Special consideration is given to hot runners for PET, not only for proper balancing but also for rearranging the layers of the flowing plastic inside the

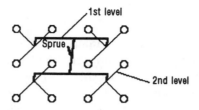

Figure 4.21   Twelve-cavity, two-level hot runner mold.

ducts at every turn to minimize differences in the acetaldehyde level within the plastic when it reaches the gates.

4.3.8 Types of Manifold Heaters

The following four methods are normally used to heat manifolds, either alone or in combinations of two or three (see Fig. 4.22): 1) cast-in heaters, 2) cartridge heaters, 3) tubular heaters, and d) band heaters.

4.3.8.1 Cast-In Heaters

Cast-in heaters were an early development in hot runner technology. Today, it is used by some commercially available hot runner systems. It consists of tubular heaters cast inside a body of aluminum or beryllium-copper alloy. The resulting heater casting is then machined and bored out for passages for the plastic (Fig. 4.22a). These heaters are very efficient, but they become very bulky for larger molds in which a group of several such castings must be assembled. The life of the heaters is very good. The control is by thermocouples, usually one per casting. However, when a heater burns out, the whole casting must be replaced.

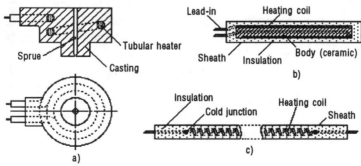

Figure 4.22   Types of heaters for manifolds: a) cast-in heater, b) cartridge heater, and c) tubular heater.

4.3.8.2 Cartridge Heaters

The cartridge heater is quite common in many hot runner systems on the market. There are, however, three problems connected with them.

First, the heat distribution along these heaters is not uniform from end to end. Heat distribution is best and most uniform for the length near the middle, but tapers off toward the end where the leads come in and similarly, but less, toward the far end (Fig. 4.22b). If such heaters must be used, they should be used in pairs with leads coming from opposite sides.

Second, cartridge heaters tend to be subject to electrical problems and to physical abuse. They are hard to remove from their bores for servicing or replacement, unless they are placed in through holes so that they can be pushed out of the bore. If cartridge heaters have to be used, there are several good ways to extend their lives:

1. Control the finish and the fit inside the heater bores to avoid development of overheated spots and burn out where they do not touch the surrounding metal (heat sink).
2. It is better to control the heat by voltage regulation, instead of on-off controls, so the heaters are not subjected to frequent impacts of full voltage but rather to a gentle variation below their rated voltage. The lower voltage also creates less arcing-over from terminal to terminal in a humid environment.
3. Temperature measurement (placing of thermocouples) is a problem because these heaters are seldom identical, even if the rating is the same. Also, the control of each individual heater influences the other heaters, which can result in uneven heat distribution throughout the distributor.

The third problem with cartridge heaters involves their wiring. This is a moldmaking and maintenance problem. Each heater needs two wires and, with many heaters, they are preferably inserted from both sides of the mold. Wiring the heater neatly and permitting easy access in case the heater must be replaced creates quite a problem.

However, a great advantage of cartridge heaters is their relatively low cost and easy availability. Also, the manifold is made at low cost by just drilling and reaming, compared to the other methods.

4.3.8.3 Tubular Heater

The tubular heater consists of a resistance coil inside a tube (sheath) of stainless steel or bronze, which is then filled with magnesium oxide powder and drawn to the specified length. During drawing, the wall thickness and diameter are reduced and the oxide is compacted so that the coil can never get close to the wall of the tube. The ends of the coil are welded to leads that come out of the ends of the tube. The ends are then capped and the lead-in wires connected to electric supply wires.

The finished tubing is quite flexible and can be bent like any tubes using appropriate fixtures. The only restrictions are a specified minimum bending radius and a certain specified distance from the junction point, called the "cold junction", where the coil joins the lead-in wire.

The advantages of these heaters are their ruggedness and the ability to form them into practically any reasonable shape that may be required for the hot runner manifold. The life expectancy is very good, but there are certain limits to their availability. Stocks of blank lengths are available in various wattages. The distance of the cold junction from the end can be specified to the supplier as required.

To use these heaters, a suitable groove is milled into the manifold on both faces, and the heater is pushed in together with heat-conducting cement, which is then smoothed out. A screwed-on cover plate may be used to prevent the heater from coming out of the groove. The heater connections are then joined in parallel with a common electrical connection. A single thermocouple controls the temperature.

The tubular heating method surpasses all others in both simplicity and in quality of temperature "evenness" throughout the plate. The cost is somewhat higher than for the other types of heaters.

4.3.8.4 Band (Mica) Heaters

The band heater (not illustrated) consists in principle of a flat heating wire coiled around a flat strip of mica. Between the coil and the body to be heated is a flat strip of mica, which is both an electrical insulator and a fairly good heat conductor. On the other side of the coil is a flat asbestos strip insulating electrically from the outside sheath and reducing heat losses to the surroundings. All of the parts are then sandwiched between two flat strips of metal, forming a sheath to protect the heater, by crimping or welding to create a solid heater assembly. The heater is then either wound around a mandrel to create a tube that can be clamped around the part which is to be heated, or, on rare occasions, the heater can be used in its flat form, clamped between heavy flat pieces of metal.

The band heater is very inexpensive and is available in many standard sizes as it is used not only in the plastics field. There are, however, a number of disadvantages when used with molds or with machines, and they are generally not recommended.

Life expectancy of these heaters can be fairly short. They are very sensitive to hot spots and burn out easily if contact with the body to be heated (heat sink) is not good. The problem is usually connected with the heater assembly and method used to clamp it to the heat sink.

Also, electrical connections are always a problem. These connections cannot be made rugged enough to withstand rough and frequent handling. Finally, efficiency is not very good, as a substantial portion of the heat is radiated away from the side opposite the heat sink.

4.3.9 Nozzles and Gates

Nozzles are the connecting links between the hot runner manifold and the gate (cavity). The essential considerations regarding nozzles are: mechanical strength to resist bursting and wear; good heat conductivity to keep the plastic hot and bring the heat as near as possible to the gate; good insulation from the surrounding, cooled mold parts; and easy access for service of nozzle and heater.

These requirements are difficult to meet. For the most heat conductivity, pure copper would be the best nozzle material, but its tensile strength is very low and it wears out easily. Usually, a copper alloy containing 2.5–3% beryllium is used for the nozzle tips; occasionally, hard tool steel is used.

A number of designs are used by the various moldmakers to reduce the heat loss to the surroundings. Usually, small contact areas between hot and cold components, long flow paths for the heat, or heat-insulating materials are provided, or combinations of these three approaches are used. It is also possible (and quite frequently done) to supply enough heat to overcome the losses caused by poor insulation, but this is unwise for economical reasons and makes temperature control more difficult.

There are essentially two types of gates: 1) open gates (pinpoint or edge gates) and 2) valved gates.

4.3.9.1 Open Gates

The open gate is the simplest and cheapest type of hot runner gate, but it is often difficult to control in operation . The principle of the open nozzle is simple: the plastic flows freely through it during injection but freezes off during the cooling portion of the cycle so that, as the mold opens to allow ejection of the product, the frozen gate prevents the plastic from oozing, or "drooling", out of the hot runner.

Figure 4.23 shows the cross section of a typical open gate. The functioning of the open nozzle is affected by several factors.

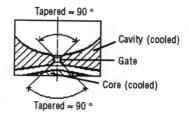

Figure 4.23   Open nozzle gate.

1. Size and shape of the gate opening: diameter, length of land, and the angles of the land on either side of the gate. Each designer or molder has his own preferences regarding these dimensions and shapes. Some work well with one type of plastics and some with others.

2. Type of the material molded: Some materials behave very well with any open gate design, some may need very accurate control and special features, and some cannot be molded at all with an open gate.

3. Operating temperature affects the viscosity of the plastic. The hotter the plastic, the easier it is to inject, but the gate will not freeze as quickly as desired.

4. Cooling temperature and quality of cooling in the gate area also affect the plastic. The better the cooling in the gate area, the faster the plastic will freeze and the less the chance of "stringing" (i.e., the plastic pulls into a fine thread reaching from the gate to the product) during the opening of the mold. This thread, or "string", which remains attached to the product, is undesirable and indicative of poor machine adjustment or poor gate or mold design. Some materials string worse than others; PS is particularly prone to string.

5. Mold open time: If the time from mold opening to mold close is short (≈ 1–2 seconds), the material does not have enough time to run out if the gate is not frozen completely. However, any interruption of the molding cycle may create a fair-sized "drool" at the gate, which may cause trouble when the molding is resumed.

6. Molding cycle: If the time between the end of injection, or "injection-hold", and the start of the next injection is too long, the plastic in the gate may freeze so that the next injection cannot dislodge the frozen slug in the gate, and the cavity will not fill. With materials such as PS, this condition can be troublesome, but it is not too serious with PE. To overcome it, in several designs heat is brought into the gate area from

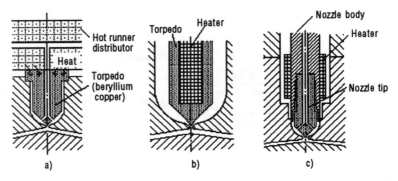

Figure 4.24   Typical torpedo designs wherein the torpedoes are heated by: a) conduction b) a cartridge heater inside the torpedo, and c) an outside band heater.

the inside of the plastic stream in the form of a "torpedo", with an extended (hot) point right into the gate opening. Such a hot point may be heated by conduction from the heat in the manifold (many European molds) or by heaters either inside the torpedo or on the outside of the nozzle that conduct the heat toward the point. See Fig. 4.24 for some typical torpedo designs. There is a wide variety of designs for these three systems of torpedoes, but the underlying principle is always the same.

7. Decompression: Plastic is compressible. During injection, the plastic inside the hot runner manifold is under high pressure and therefore compressed by approximately 1% of its volume. At the end of the injection cycle, this compressed volume of plastic inside the runner has only two ways to flow: either back toward the machine nozzle or into the mold through the gate after the mold opens. If the gate is not well frozen, the plastic will drool into the cavity. The molding machine can be controlled, if properly equipped, by setting it so that the screw pulls back at the end of the injection cycle (or injection-hold) to let the compressed plastic expand into the extruder, called "suck back".

The hot runner system can be equipped with a decompression sprue bushing where the machine nozzle is seated on the mold sprue. When the machine nozzle pulls back at the end of the injection cycle, the expanding plastic pushes the bushing back and relieves pressure inside the hot runner (Fig. 4.25).

8. Experience: Because of the many factors affecting proper operation of this type of gating, it is best used only by an experienced operator.

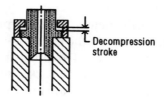

Figure 4.25   Decompression sprue bushing.

Lack of experience is probably the main reason (rather than the additional cost compared to cold runner molds) why the American market was so long in accepting the hot runner molding technology.

4.3.9.2 Valved Gates

The valved gate is a further development of the gate technology in that it provides external mechanical control of the plastic flow through the gate. There are numerous designs, and we will discuss here only the essential features of the valve gating principle.

The basic feature of the valve gate is a pin that reaches into the gate. When in the forward position, the pin closes the gate; when in its rear position, the pin opens the gate. The method of pin operation is different for the various designs, and we will illustrate some of them without going into details (Fig. 4.26).

Figure 4.26a shows a valve gate in which the valve pin is spring-loaded to close the gate. The valve pin has a basic diameter, D, and a reduced diameter, d,

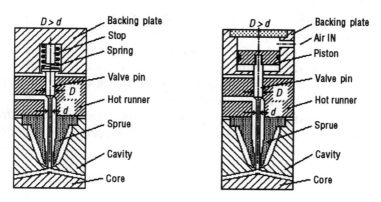

Figure 4.26   Pin operation of a) a spring-loaded valve gate.and b) an air piston (one-sided) valve gate.

near the gate. During injection, the pressure of the plastic acts on the area difference created by these two diameters, forces the pin away from the gate, and lets the plastic flow into the cavity. At the end of the injection cycle, when the pressure is reduced or ceases completely, the spring drives the pin forward to seal the gate. The system is simple, but the drawback is the lack of control over the spring pressure. If the injection pressure is too low for a certain spring force, the valve will not open. This can be important when low injection-hold pressure is required to maintain flow of plastic into the mold during the cooling and shrinking of the plastic within the cavity.

The valve gate in Fig. 4.26b has an air cylinder and piston. This varies from the first system by using air pressure to force the pin toward the gate. It is more complicated but permits control of the force exerted on the pin. The air pressure can be on permanently so that the air acts like a spring; since the pressure can be controlled, the force can also be easily controlled.

Better yet is to control not only the air pressure but also its timing. The air pressure is switched off during injection and switched on when the injection or injection-hold pressure is ended. This timing control avoids some pressure drop at the gate by eliminating the need to overcome the spring pressure.

Some systems use hydraulics for the control of valve pins, but there is a risk in using oil within a mold because of the fire hazard when using flammable oils in the vicinity of the electric heaters. Also, there is a risk of oil leaks and contamination in the molding area.

Other actuation methods include externally operated cams or levers that control either individual valve pins or groups of them.

A type of valve gate that is not illustrated is one in which the valve pin is air-operated in both directions. In such a system, the valve pin has no change in diameter, and the pressure of the plastic does not move the pin. The pins are pushed forward to close and pulled back to open the gate through the use of double-acting air cylinders or cams.

The advantage of a two-sided system is that the valve pin can be retracted before injection starts, thus letting the plastic flow freely into the cavity without pressure drop. The force and timing of the closing is controllable. The disadvantage of this system is the added complexity and cost.

There are also mechanical methods of moving the valve pin in both directions with hydraulically operated positive cams. This, however, is quite complicated mechanically and rarely used.

4.3.9.3 Hot Runner Edge Gate

Figure 4.27 shows a typical hot runner edge gate. This is an open gate in a hot runner system; therefore, the same list of considerations apply as for the open pinpoint gate. A hot runner edge gate can be used where it is not permissible or where it is impractical to provide a hot runner gate in the top surface of the product. A typical example is the Petri dish, which must not have a gate mark in its top surface because of the optical requirements for use of the product.

As the mold opens, the product stays with the core and shears the gate. To prevent jetting (flow) marks on the surface of the product, the gate should be facing a solid obstacle, such as the core, to disperse the inrushing plastic flow rather than let it flow freely into the open cavity space. The length of the land should be less than the space, t, between the cavity and core opposite the gate to permit (during injection) the frozen plastic slug in the gate to be carried into the cavity space, where it will melt and disappear in the fresh plastic.

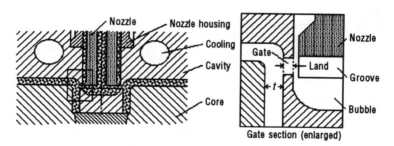

Figure 4.27 Hot runner edge gate.

It is also important to bring heat right to the gate without losing heat to the cooled cavity block. Figure 4.27 shows a widening of the nozzle near the gate. The gap between the nozzle and the steel of the cavity block should be ≈ 0.1 mm. The nozzle reaches slightly below the gate, and the plastic flows in a groove toward the gate. Further up, the body is smaller in diameter so that the injected plastic can create an insulating sleeve around it. The nozzle is heated, similar to the methods shown in Fig. 4.25 (p. 73), by either conduction from the manifold or outside heaters, similar to the nozzle tip. A plastic "bubble" at the end of the nozzle insulates against heat loss to the cavity block.

It is preferable to have one nozzle feed two gates, as shown, to balance the reaction forces on the nozzle exerted by the plastic flow during injection. Such forces tend to deflect the nozzle away from the gate. However, one gate per nozzle can also work successfully if the reaction force is taken up by a solid stop pin opposite the gate or if the nozzle is stiff enough to resist the deflection. If the molded article is small enough or if its shape is appropriate, more than two gates can be fed from one nozzle. This would be the case in small lids for vials, in bodies for syringes, etc.

The vestige produced by this gate is similar to the gate mark from tunnel gating. The size is about 0.7 mm Ø, depending on the material injected.

The main problems with hot runner edge gates are:

1. Strength of the cavity around the gate: Since the land must be kept short, there is sometimes insufficient strength in the cavity wall at the gate. There are a number of designs which deal with this problem more or less successfully, but to describe them here is outside the scope of this book.
2. Adequate between too much heat, resulting in drooling, or not enough heat, resulting in freezing.
3. Gate wear: The gate is delicate and easily damaged by frequent cleaning, clearing of a frozen slug, or from the shearing action if the plastic is hard or abrasive.

To date, there is no edge gate with valving, as there is with pinpoint nozzles.

4.3.10 Warm Runners

Throughout this text, we have occasionally referred to the molding of thermosets. Before the incredible rise in the use of thermoplastics, thermosets occupied a large portion of the plastics industry. Many improvements to the thermoset molding technology were made with regard to automation of the process and improvements of the raw materials to allow faster molding and reduce labor cost.

Only after the development of hot runners for thermoplastics did that section of the industry which was still involved with thermoset molding try to develop an equivalent method for thermosets. However, the range of products that would lend themselves economically to "runnerless" molding (as hot runner molding is sometimes called) is very limited and mainly includes only small products made from phenolics, alkyds, and some rubbers. As a result, the development of warm runner molds is lagging behind, and there is little published in this field.

We will, therefore, not go into design details but rather list the important considerations for designing warm runner molds:

1. Temperature control from extruder to gate must be very accurate to prevent scorching of the material.

2. Accessibility to the runner system to remove runners at the end of a production run (or in case of interruptions) must be easy.
3. Thermal insulation is necessary from the relatively cold machine platen and from the heated mold. The mold is heated to a much higher temperature to achieve fast curing in the cavity; this could influence the runner system.
4. Nozzle area is of particular importance because of the unavoidable contact of two elements with different temperatures. The nozzle forms part of the runner system; the gate is part of the mold.
5. Plastic Flow: Because of the higher viscosity of thermosets, the passages must be larger than those used for thermoplastics.

4.4 Cooling and Heating

The need for heat exchange has been summarized in Section 3.2.3 on heat exchange (p. 30), so we will only point out again how the quality of cooling will affect the mold cost.

Earlier molds had only superficial cooling within the cavity and core mounting plates. This is cheap and results in long cycle times and high product costs. However, as pointed out in Section 4.1, Number of Cavities, there are cases, especially with very low production molds, where such minimal cooling can be economically justified.

To reduce the cycle time, the cooling must become more sophisticated. Drilled cooling channels in cavity and core blocks and especially in inserts are very efficient and usually well worth the added mold cost. The only serious consideration before carrying this to extremes is the need to maintain proper strength of the mold components, which must therefore always be considered if the added complexity of some cooling is worth the gains that can be achieved in cycle time (point of diminishing returns).

Good cooling is expensive. The quality of cooling will affect the molding cycle. It is up to the designer, together with the molder, to find the optimum quality of cooling.

NOTE: Anything said above about cooling also may be applied to thermosets by exchanging the "cooling" for "heating", except that a heat is absolutely required for thermosets to cure the material; an injection mold will function even without cooling, but only very slowly, by radiating the heat into the surroundings.

4.5 Ejection Methods

After the mold opens, the molded product(s) must be removed from the mold. This process can be done fully manually, manually with the assistance of ejector mechanisms, or fully automatically.

4.5.1 Manual Ejection

Some products can be removed from the mold by just blowing air at the product near the parting line without the help of ejectors. The air cools and shrinks the product, enters between the product and the core (or cavity), and lifts the product, which is then removed by hand, sometimes with the help of a soft but sharp-edged tool (usually brass or aluminum) so as not to damage the mold. This method is still used when molding tires or for thermoset dinnerware, which must not be dropped; it is also used with some injection molds, parts permitting (e.g., with accordionlike sleeves made from elastomers). Manual ejection is certainly cheap from the point of view mold cost, but it requires an operator. Since the cycle times can be long (1–5 min or even longer), one operator can serve several machines so that the labor content is not as high as it would appear.

4.5.2 Machine Ejector Mechanisms

The presence of an ejector mechanism does not imply automatic ejection. It means only that the molded product is lifted or stripped from the core by some mechanical means.

Injection molding machines are always provided with ejection mechanisms on the clamp side as standard equipment. However, in some cases, ejectors must also be provided on the stationary side. This can be done by linking the ejector mechanism with chains or similar lost motion links to the opening motion of the clamp or by an independent hydraulically (oil or air) actuated mechanism located either in the hot platen or in the mold itself. This last method (with air) is very common with stack molds, where one set of cores is in that mold half which is mounted on the stationary platen. Compression molding machines are usually equipped with ejectors on both cavity and core sides of the mold and machine.

The pattern of the location of ejector rod holes in the platens is standardized in the USA and in Europe. However, there are manufacturers who have their own patterns or a mixture of the standard and their proprietary patterns.

We will next consider the following four mechanical ejection methods: 1) bumper ejection, 2) hydraulic ejection, 3) ejection with linkages, and 4) air cylinder ejection.

4.5.2.1 Bumper Ejection

This ejection method is based on fixed, adjustable stops—"bumpers" or "ejector rods"—on the clamp housing. These bumpers pass through the holes in the platen; at a certain point during the clamp opening stroke, they contact the mold ejector plate and start ejecting the products (Fig. 4.28). The bumper method is very simple but can be used only in molding machines with fixed, repetitive opening stroke.

The end of the ejector rod is at a fixed point. If the opening stroke of the machine were increased, the end of the rod would penetrate deeper into the mold. Since the travel of the mold ejector plate is limited by the mold construction, the increased stroke could cause the mold to be pushed off the moving platen by breaking the mounting screws. If the stroke were decreased, the products might not completely eject.

The adjustment of the ejector rods is very critical. The bumpers must be not only of the proper length (see above) but also all of the same length to ensure that all bumpers contact the ejector plate at the same moment to avoid cocking of the ejector plate and possible damage to the mold.

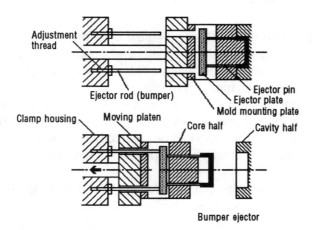

Figure 4.28   Bumper ejection: a) mold closed and b) mold open.

The best arrangement is to use four (never less than three) bumpers arranged in a widely spaced pattern; this reduces the risk of cocking of the ejector plate. The location must match the available ejector pattern of the machine used. This is of special concern when a mold is to be used on several different machines.

Size of bumpers depends on the forces encountered when stripping. Usually, there is no choice, since the size of the mounting of the bumpers (screw threads in the clamp housing) is determined by the machine used.

The ejector plate (in the moving mold) can approach the bumpers quite rapidly, and the ensuing impact is not only noisy but can cause damage to the mold and also to the products. This is often the case if, during ejection, the vacuum between the product and the core is not broken fast enough so that a portion of the product adheres to the core while the rest is pushed out. In such cases, venting the inside of the product is indispensable.

The clamp speed always slows down toward the fully open position. This is inherent with toggle clamps due to the geometry of the clamp mechanism. With hydraulic clamps, the slow-down is achieved with hydraulic methods. However, in both these clamps systems, the platens move rapidly while still some distance away from the fully open position. If a long ejection stroke is required, the bumpers may contact the ejector plate while the clamp moves too fast; the only remedy then is to slow down the clamp opening speed and increase the cycle time.

For shallow products (i.e., with little ejection stroke required) and with low speeds, the bumper method is quite satisfactory.

4.5.2.2 Hydraulic Ejection

The salient feature of this method is that the ejection mechanism is part of the moving platen and is independent of the clamp stroke. Today, all machines are equipped with hydraulic ejectors that use either one central or two side-mounted cylinders to actuate a machine ejector plate.

The connection to the mold ejector plate is made with push rods, which pass through the standard or proprietary pattern of ejector holes on the platens. Occasionally, the push rods also can be fastened in the mold ejector plate, and the ejection mechanism not only acts as pusher but also is used to return the mold ejector plate.

The stroke of the ejection can be regulated within its design limits. The start of the ejection stroke can be timed where it is most suitable for the operation, and it can limit the ejection force and velocity by regulation of the hydraulic pressure and flow, respectively.

4.5.2.3 Ejection with Linkages

By using appropriate linkages to connect the mold ejector plate with the stationary mold half, the ejection motion can be operated using the motion of the mold. Although the applications for this method are limited, they have the advantage of being very accurate, noiseless, and gentle. Linkages also require a fairly accurate and repetitive mold opening stroke.

4.5.2.4 Air Cylinder Ejection

Occasionally, for stack molds which require ejection from the stationary mold platen (which have no machine ejector mechanism), air cylinders can be added to the platen or incorporated into the mold itself to operate the ejectors from this side. They may also be necessary in single-level molds when two-stage ejection is required, in which case both ejection motions must be independently controlled.

4.5.2.5 Combinations of Ejection Mechanisms

It is quite common to use in one mold combinations of ejector actuations, such as bumpers and hydraulic ejectors; hydraulic and lever ejectors ; hydraulic and air cylinder ejectors; hydraulic, air cylinder, and levers, etc.

4.5.3 Mold Ejection Mechanisms

Mold ejection systems, also called "knockout" systems, are used to remove the product from the mold after the mold has opened. There are several systems used, and we will explain the more important features of some of them.

4.5.3.1 Ejector Pins

Figure 4.29 shows various terms used with pin ejection. The "parallels" which surround the ejector box on at least two sides are often so far apart that the core plate is not sufficiently supported under the cores. In such cases, "support pillars" must be installed between the core backing plate and the mold mounting plate; these pillars pass through the ejector and retainer plate. In some instances, usually with large ejector plates, these pillars (with bushings) guide the ejector plate. The system is simple and has a relatively low cost.

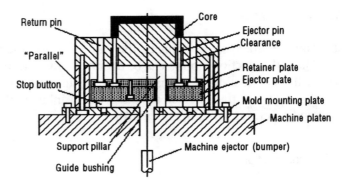

Figure 4.29   Pin ejection.

Stop buttons are installed to take up the forces from the injection pressure acting on the ends of the ejector pins. They can be used for final adjustment of the ejector pin length.

Some smaller machines do not require ejector boxes for small molds. The moving platen has a central opening large enough to accommodate the ejector plate. In such cases, the ejector plate must be "suspended" from the core plate, and the injection force on the ejector pins is taken up by the heads of the bolts used to suspend the ejector plate.

4.5.3.2   Stripper Plate

Figure 4.30 shows the core side of a stripper plate mold in its simplest form. After a certain travel of the mold open stroke, the machine ejector rods start pushing the stripper plate forward and strip the product off the core. The stroke of the stripper plate should be limited to keep it from falling off the core; also, it must

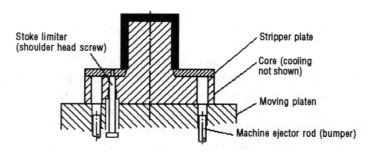

Figure 4.30   Stripper plate ejection.

be guided so that it will not touch and scratch the core. In a cheap execution, shoulder head screws are used, but it is better to provide proper guide pins (see Fig. 4.33, p. 84) which may be constructed so that they also act as stroke limiters (not shown).

4.5.3.3 Stripper Rings

A stripper plate in its simplest form is a plate with circular bores which surround the circular base of the core. Because the stripper plate slides over the core during ejection and return, cylindrical bores will score and seize after very few operations and, therefore, should not be used, even in cheap molds (Fig. 4.31).

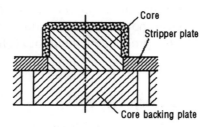

Figure 4.31   Stripper plate.

The best method is to make the base of the core tapered, with matching tapered bores in the stripper plate. In this case, the surfaces do not slide past each other, but the plate is lifted off the core. However, such tapered bores in usually rectangular plates are difficult to produce; this leads to the introduction of stripper rings, as shown in Fig. 4.32. The outside of the stripper ring is cylindrical where it fits into the plate, which is no problem to produce.

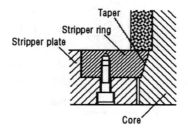

Figure 4.32   Stripper ring.

There are numerous methods of holding the stripper ring in the stripper plate; they will not be shown here. The method shown (screws) is low cost compared with others. The ring can be made floating in the stripper plate, which is of special advantage in multicavity molds, especially when heat expansion is a problem. However, with edge gating, where the runners must cross the joint between ring and plate, no gap is permitted. This prevents the plastic from flashing into the gap.

The taper in the core and in the stripper ring is in most cases circular, which is fairly easy to produce on conventional tool room equipment. Occasionally, the shape of the taper follows the shape of the core, but this is very expensive, even if it can be produced on milling machines and grinders that can follow a model or that can be programmed to generate the odd shape on both the core and the ring.

Sometimes, the stripper ring can be laid out in relation to the part so that a sufficiently large and balanced portion of the product is located over a round stripper ring that will eject the product even without following the product all around (see Fig. 4.34).

4.5.3.4 Stripper Ring Inside a Cavity–Core Stack

In a cavity-core stack, each stripper ring is surrounded by the core (as shown in Fig.4.33), or sometimes by the cavity, and cannot be tied in to a stripper plate as shown earlier. In this case, the stripper ring is connected by push rods to an ejector plate located in an ejector box, which is similar to the ejector pin arrangement, except that there is no need for stop pins.

In this arrangement in the case of multicavity molds, the influence of heat expansion or inaccuracies in location becomes insignificant. Numerous designs

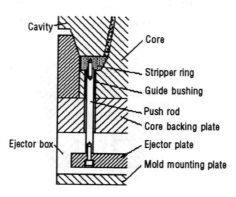

Figure 4.33   Stripper ring inside core.

are in use which will not be shown here; they are all based on the same basic principle.

4.5.3.5 Stripper Bar

Stripper bars are a variation of the stripper ring. They are commonly used where a round or shaped stripper ring would not be practical. This is often the case with larger rectangular shaped cavities or where a number of small rectangular shapes are in line in the mold so that one pair of bars can be used to eject a number of products.

The stripper bars are located under two opposing edges of the molded product. Good stripper bar design must use taper fit on the core. A mold for a rectangular shape (e.g., a box) with a wide rim and a small ratio of length over width is easier to produce with a round stripper ring (Fig. 4.34a). If the rim is narrow or there are several parts to eject, stripper bars are preferable, even if costlier (Fig. 4.34b,c).

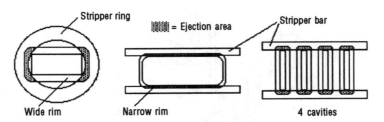

Figure 4.34   Variations of stripper rings and bars: a) round stripper ring for a wide-rimmed rectangular mold, b) stripper bars under narrow-rimmed rectangular mold edges, and c) stripper bars used with many small elongated shapes.

4.5.3.6 Preload

To ensure good seating between the tapered faces of core and stripper, the size of the bore in the ring must be slightly smaller than the size of the core. When the stripper ring is positioned over the taper in the core, it will not go down fully; it is stretched when the mold is clamped for a perfect fit and a tight seal into which plastic cannot flash during injection.

The amount of preload is measured by the length of travel of the ring from the point where it touches without load to where it comes to rest in the clamped down position. The amount of preload depends the taper angle, ring size, molding speed, and the core and ring material; past performance of similar designs are usually the best source of information. Excessive preload will result in early wear of the tapers; insufficient preload will soon flash and generate scrap.

4.5.3.7 Sleeve Ejectors

Sleeve ejectors are used in tubular products where strippers cannot be used or where holes are molded in a boss, such as shown in Fig. 4.35.

Sleeve ejectors perform two essential functions:

1. The plastic will not fill the deep, tubular shape unless there is a vent at the bottom. The sleeve provides an ideal, natural, self-cleaning vent. (See also Section 3.2.5, Venting).
2. It would be very difficult to eject the product unless it is pushed out from the lowest point of the plastic in the core. Ejectors in the flat portion of the product could pierce the product during ejection or break off the flat portion and leave the boss in the mold.

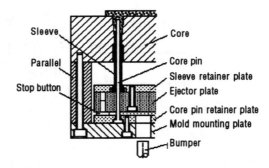

Figure 4.35   Ejector sleeve.

There is theoretically no limit to the size of sleeve ejectors; most of the applications require small sizes with inside diameters of 1–20 mm, which are available in standard sizes from moldmaker supply houses such as DME or HASCO.

Sleeves, especially when the difference between inside and outside diameter is small, are quite delicate and easily damaged and should be used only where there is no alternative. Sometimes, small changes in the product design may allow the molder to select the next larger sleeve and increase its strength. Ejector plates with delicate sleeves and small ejector pins should always be guided, as shown schematically in Fig. 4.29, (p.82).

4.5.3.8   Returning the Ejector Mechanism

4.5.3.8.1   Stripper Plate Mold   It is not absolutely necessary to provide means to return a stripper plate after ejection. As the mold closes, the cavity will push the stripper plate back, but while this is cheap, it is only practical where the speed of the clamp at the moment of impact between cavity and stripper is low. In a good mold, the stripper plate is always returned before the mold is closed.

4.5.3.8.2   Ejector Pin Mold   In addition to a positive return, an ejector pin mold also must have return pins, which ensure that the ejector pins cannot touch (and damage) the cavity in case the ejector plate is not fully returned. If large ejector pins are used as "edge ejectors" where only a small portion of the pin face acts to eject the product and the rest contacts the cavity block outside the cavity, there is no need for additional return pins.

4.5.3.8.3   Return Springs   Stripper plate return springs may be installed either inside or outside the mold. For a return spring inside the mold, the space for the spring and its length depends mainly on the thickness of the core plate (Fig. 4.36a). For long life, the maximum permissible compression of any spring is between 15 and 25% of its length. The stroke length is therefore usually very limited; inside springs are only practical for shallow products. Another disadvantage is that the mold may run with a broken spring, which cannot be seen from the outside. Inspection and replacement of the spring requires removing the mold from the machine.

For return springs outside the mold, the springs can be long (Fig. 4.36b). If possible and necessary, the stripper plate may be extended and the springs placed alongside the moving platen.

In either case, it is good practice to use four springs in a rectangular pattern, spread as far as possible, regardless of whether a center ejector or four outside

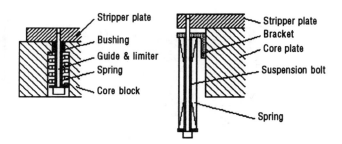

Figure 4.36   Stripper plate return springs mounted: a) inside the mold and b) outside the mold.

ejectors are used. Frequently, in low-cost molds, one center return spring is used to reach into the hole for the center machine ejector. Such a center spring can usually be long enough for long spring life, but it too cannot be seen from the outside.

4.5.3.8.4   Return Air Cylinders   Such air cylinders can be used instead of return springs. A spring can be used for a stroke of only 15–25% of its installed length if it must last a reasonably long time. An equivalent length of an air cylinder can be used for virtually all of its length. Also, while the spring force increases linearly as the spring is compressed, the force exerted by an air cylinder is constant over the whole stroke and depends only on the area of the piston and the air pressure.

With shorter strokes, the cylinders can be machined into the core plate (Fig. 4.37). This design can also be modified by bringing in a second air line below the piston and using it as an ejector piston as well as for the return of the stripper plate. The bottom opening must then be properly sealed so that the air cannot leak out. This is frequently done when ejectors are required in the cavity side of the mold.

For a long stroke, the cylinder can be located in the center hole of the moving platen if the opening is large enough. Figure 4.38 shows a typical design for such a cylinder.

Both methods—return springs or return air cylinders—for the *stripper* plates also can be used as return mechanism for *ejector* plates. Note that the use of *air* cylinders for ejection is not always a good solution. If accurate and controllable ejection force and speed is required, *hydraulic* cylinders should be used to actuate the ejector plate.

4.5.3.8.5   Return of Mold Ejectors with Hydraulic Machine Ejectors   With most molds, the ejector plate is pushed forward during ejection by one of the

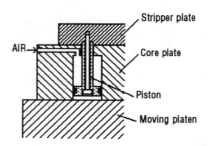

Figure 4.37   Return cylinder machined into the core plate.

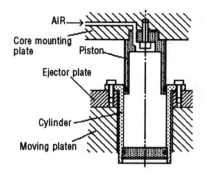

Figure 4.38 Typical cylinder mounted in center of moving platen with sealed bottom opening beneath ejector piston.

methods of machine ejectors described earlier. The ejector plate is returned by the force of internal or external return springs or air cylinders in the mold, as explained above. With ejector pins or sleeves, safety return pins make sure that these usually delicate parts do not project into the mold space or touch and damage the cavity side of the mold.

With some molds, it may be advantageous to tie the ejector plate to the hydraulic machine ejector so that the ejector plate is pulled back when the ejector returns. This eliminates the need for return springs; however, this method must be used with caution. It still requires return pins to ensure safety of the mold, but there is a danger of personal injury to anyone servicing the mold in the machine in case of a hydraulic or electric malfunction affecting the ejection cylinders—fingers may be trapped between the moving ejector plate and the mold plates.

4.5.3.9 Air Ejection

Pressurized air is used to eject, without the use of air cylinders to operate ejectors or strippers, although in some cases mechanical ejection is used in addition to the air ejection. Figure 4.39 shows schematically a simple method of air ejection. In Fig. 4.39a, the poppet is in its molding position; it is returned to its seat with a spring, either by an air cylinder or from an ejector plate, before injection. During injection, the plastic pressure keeps the poppet seated so that plastic cannot enter the air channels. When the mold opens, the poppet is pushed forward, either by the air pressure or by an ejector plate. The poppet lifts the product a short distance, and air enters the core at or near the bottom of the product and lifts it off the core.

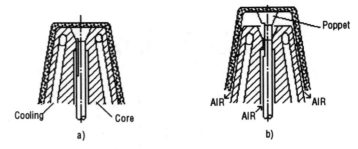

Figure 4.39   Air ejection using pressurized air: a) with the poppet returned to its seat in the molding position and b) with the poppet pushed forward when the mold opens.

If there is not enough draft in the product, the gap between the core and the product may be so small that the escaping air (Fig. 4.39b) creates a flow effect, which tends to keep the product floating a certain distance away from the core without letting it fall. Sometimes, such "suction" can be avoided by finding the proper air pressure; in other cases, the location of the air gap or the stroke of the poppet must be changed to make this method trouble free.

A more recent method, not illustrated, is as follows: The ejection air blows through a precisely sized slot on the circumference part way down the core. The slot is fixed and resembles a venting gap; it is narrow enough that the plastic cannot enter but wide enough that compressed air can. This method permits very fast molding and is simple in its principle, but it requires a composite core and quite a complicated layout of the cooling and air channels within the core.

For some products, especially deep containers and those with little side draft, a combination of both methods of air ejection is used. The air escaping at the side of the core creates an air cushion, which permits the product to slide easily off the core, while the poppet allows air to enter the product from the center for fast ejection.

4.5.3.10 Two-Stage Ejection

Occasionally, there is the need to provide two separate ejection strokes. We will illustrate one of the many cases encountered. It is also possible to provide three-stage ejection, but we will not go into it here.

A typical need for two-stage ejection arises when a product has an internal rib that could not be ejected with ordinary means, such as ejector pins or sleeves. Figure 4.40 shows an example: The stripper plate alone could not eject the inner rib; the force exerted by the stripper on the outer shell would tend to distort the product and cause the inner rib to break off. The separation between the inner core and the ring permits good venting, which is self-cleaning during the stripping motion. The actuation is simple: the first ejection stroke (Fig. 4.40b) lifts the product and the stripper plate to pull the core out of the inner portion of the product. The second ejection (Fig. 4.40c) lifts the product free from the ring and permits it to drop.

There are numerous combinations of possibilities and many designs to combine mechanical and air-actuated ejectors in two- or three-stage ejection arrangements. To elaborate on them would exceed the scope of this book.

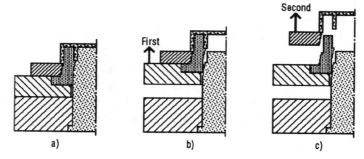

a)   b)   c)

Figure 4.40   A typical two-stage ejection process: a) the mold in the closed position, b) the first ejection stroke, and c) the second ejection stroke.

4.5.3.11 Ejection of Products with Inside Undercuts

For products with simple undercuts and for some materials (e.g., PE) in configurations such as lids for containers, it is possible to push, or "strip" the product off the core over an undercut, provided the product design is suitable for such stripping. Occasionally, the core cannot be withdrawn from the product because of projections into the plastic (e.g., internal threads or other types of (technical) undercuts).

If stripping or unscrewing is not practical or possible, the core can be designed as a "collapsible core". Such a core consists of several moving sections which can slide inside the basic core. Before ejection, they slide toward each other in such a way that they "relieve" the undercut(s). When the mold closes, these sections move apart again to form the desired shape of the core. During injection, these moving parts must not present any gaps into which plastic could enter. Also, they must be internally backed up (by a wedge or wedges) so that the pressure exerted by the plastic during injection cannot dislodge them. It can be easily seen that such collapsible cores are rather difficult to design, build, and maintain, and they are used only where there is no alternative.

4.5.3.12 Ejection of Inside-Threaded Products

Three methods are commonly used to eject inside-thread products from the mold:

1. Stripping the cap off the core, without damage to the thread or the product, may be possible using a stripper plate. The threads must be shallow enough or of such design that the product will slip out of the thread-forming configuration, or "groove" in the core. Also, it must be possible to stretch the material without breaking it. The thread should consist of no more than one turn so that once the thread is lifted out of its groove, it will not be allowed to snap into a successive groove.

    Usually, the only materials used for such caps are PE and PP; there are, however cases, where PS or other stiff materials are stripped from the core. This is possible either when the ratio between the part diameter and the amount of stretching required is high, so the allowable percentage elongation of the material is not exceeded, or by controlling the molding cycle so that the product is still hot when stripped and sufficiently elastic.

2. Collapsible cores may be used; refer to Section 4.5.3.11 for discussion. This method is rarely used with products of less than 75 mm in diameter (e.g., high-quality jar caps, etc.)

3. Unscrewing is the standard method for such products as tooth paste tube caps, liquor bottle caps, etc. There are two distinctly different methods used to produce these products, and each method has been executed in a number of ways. We will describe just the salient features of each. Threads for unscrewing must always terminate at the end of the core, called "run out", to permit the molded thread to be unscrewed from the core.

4.5.3.12.1 Rotating Core Unscrewing Method   The molded product is held in a fixed position, while the core rotates to screw itself out of the cap. To do this, the cap design must include some "teeth" molded by a gripper ring (Fig. 4.41) which prevent the cap from rotating while the core unscrews and retracts. The final ejection of the product is then accomplished by ejectors (strippers) in the core or by retraction of the grippers so that the products can fall off the core mounting plate.

Rotating core molds have been built for any number of cavities from 1 to 48, or more. The disadvantages of this method are:

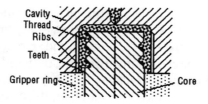

Figure 4.41   Rotating core with gripper ring teeth for unscrewing threaded products.

1. Complex and expensive driving mechanisms are required for the cores. These are usually rack and pinion drives that use hydraulic cylinders to move the racks. A complex mechanism is required as part of each mold (high mold cost).
2. Core cooling is often insufficient. For fastest production, the cooling of the core is more important than the cavity cooling. Because the cores rotate and sometimes even contain ejector pins, the core cooling is often insufficient and results in longer cycle times.
3. Product design must include some internal teeth, either inside the rim at the open end or at the bottom of the cap. This may be objected to by the designer of the end product.
4. Spacing of cavities in the mold is restricted due to the space required for the drive mechanism for each cavity.
5. Maintenance is very difficult. There are many rotating and sliding fits inside the mold which either cannot (too complicated) or should not be lubricated because of contamination. Molds require frequent disassembly for cleaning of grease at the molding surfaces. Also, repairs to rotating seals are frequent to eliminate water leaks. Cores are expensive and difficult to repair.
6. Product cost is usually higher than with the fixed core method.

There are, however, advantages to the rotating core method, which are as follows:

1. Standard injection molding machines can be used, provided the platens are large enough to accommodate the usually large mold and to provide room for the external drive.
2. Outside shape of a cap is not restricted. The product may be perfectly round and smooth on the outside or have the parting line elsewhere than at the open end of the thread. For example, the cap could have a ball shape with inside threads.

4.5.3.12.2   Fixed Core Unscrewing Method   After the products are molded and the mold opens, a set of unscrewing cups slide simultaneously over the product, engage into external ribs of the caps, and start to unscrew the caps from the cores (Fig. 4.42). To be economically viable, the mold must be equipped with two identical mold core plates which swing around one tie bar of the machine. While one plate is inside the mold for molding, the other one is outside facing the unscrewing mechanism.

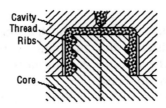

Figure 4.42   Fixed core with unscrewing cups that engage ribs to unscrew the caps from the core.

Disadvantages of this system:

1.   A special machine is required. A swinging mechanism to alternate the two sets of plates and "unscrewing heads" for the mechanical unscrewing action must be provided. If any mold designated for a machine has the same cavity layout, one head is sufficient. If the layout or the number of cavities changes, additional heads are required. The cost of such setup is only justifiable if the production runs are very high.
2.   Product design is restricted, as products must either have ribs on the circumference where the unscrewing cups can get a good grip, or some special provisions to this effect must be provided in the product. Products with an offset parting line or with smooth outside cannot be molded easily in this design. There is also a limit of the amount of draft on the outside of the cap; the ribs may become disengaged before the products are fully unscrewed. Generally, each product needs special scrutiny to decide whether it can be molded trouble-free on this system.

Advantages of this system:

1.   Spacing of cavities can be as close as the strength of the cavity walls will permit. The layout is usually in a square or rectangular pitch, but

odd arrangements are also possible. This allows the molder to put many more cavities in such a mold than in one with rotating cores of equivalent size.

2. Core cooling is not adversely affected. Since the cores are not moving, the best possible cooling can be provided for an often spectacular gain in cycle time.

3. The mold is very simple because all the moving mechanisms are outside of the mold as part of the machine. The mold usually does not require any additional ejection mechanism.

4. A minimum of mold maintenance is required because of its simplicity.

5. Productivity is very high because of the larger number of cavities and the reduced cycle times due to the better cooling.

6. Mold cost is not greatly affected. The additional cost of the second core plate is less, or comparable, to the costs saved by not requiring an unscrewing mechanism inside the mold.

7. Despite the higher cost of the machine, in view of the above listed advantages, the product cost compares very favorably with products molded on molds with rotating cores.

4.6   Selection of Mold Materials

The selection of materials for the construction of molds is greatly influenced by the production requirements. It is obvious that a mold which is only to produce relatively few products during its life will not require the use of long lasting materials normally associated with high production molds.

There are essentially five considerations in the selection of the materials for the cavities and cores, which are exposed to high pressures used during the injection (or compression) process:

1. They must not collapse or change dimensions under these high pressures.

2. They must able to withstand the clamp force of the machine without damage to the parting line.

3. They must resist wear by the plastic.

4. They must be able to conduct the heat away from the thermoplastic or to conduct heat to the thermosets.

5. The cost must be reasonable.

For injection molding of thermoplastics, conditions 1, 2 and 3 are fairly easy to achieve with most materials, provided certain precautions are observed. Molds can be, and have been, built from the following materials:

hardwood
plastic
mixtures of plastics and powdered metals
aluminum
zinc alloys
bronze, including beryllium-copper
mild steel
prehardened steel
case-hardening tool steels
electrodeposited nickel
through-hardening tool steels
tungsten-carbides
stainless steels

Condition 4 above may eliminate several materials, depending on the plastic. Because of the poor heat conductivity of wood and plain plastics, these materials are not suitable for thermosets, and may be used only to a very limited degree for experimental injection molds for thermoplastics.

Condition 5 is obvious. It should, however, be remembered that the least expensive material does not necessarily mean the least expensive molded product. A material may be cheap to buy but very difficult to machine or may need frequent replacement, while a better material would stand up much longer and require lower mold costs in the long run.

There are many molds, usually for limited production only or for experiments, which are built from mixtures of plastics (usually epoxies) and powdered aluminum to provide a (limited) degree of heat conductivity. They can be cast using plaster of Paris or wooden models and can be machined easily for cooling lines and for mounting in a mold shoe.

Aluminum is used practically in all blow molds, partly because of the ease of machining but mostly because of the weight factor (its weight is only one-third that of steel) and its excellent heat conductivity. For the same reasons, there are also injection molds made from aluminum. To provide strength (requirements 1, 2, and 3 above), they are often provided with steel reinforcements in critical areas (gates, parting lines) and are sometimes also backed up by steel chases to resist the compressive loads.

Zinc alloys (Zamak, etc.) and bronze are frequently used, especially in the toy industry, when the life and the total number of products coming from the mold is limited and when it is relatively easy to produce cavities (and often cores as well) by a casting process from models. The machining to finish these castings is usually limited to touch-up of the parting lines and to the drilling of cooling channels and the machining for the securing in the mold shoe. Casting does not lend itself to the production of molds for products with close dimensional tolerances. The advantage of using these castings is their low cost, the relatively short time to get into production, and their good heat conductivity. Areas of wear such as gates may require steel inserts; pins and other delicate projections are usually made from steel.

Mild steel cavities and cores are occasionally used but offer little, if any, advantage in machining or cost.

Free cutting, prehardened steels (about 30–35 Rc) can be machined faster and easier than the mild steels and offer the advantage of greater resistance against wear and compressive forces. Most large cavities and cores today are built from these steels. They do not require the added expenses of heat treatment, which includes the handling to and from the heat treat, and some finishing operations (e.g., grinding) after heat treatment.

The life of these mold components is as good as if they were made from hardened steels, with the exception of areas exposed to the wear by the plastic itself (gates), shut-off areas, and sliding fits. In these cases, hardened steel inserts or bronze wear plates are used to protect the prehardened steel and to facilitate maintenance.

Heat conductivity of prehardened steel is not as good as aluminum or bronze and very little better than tool steels. If required, bronze inserts can be used to improve the cooling process locally .

Case-hardening tool steels were, and still are, used occasionally in medium-sized cavities and cores or in small-sized hobbings for cavities. Their use in medium-sized cavities and cores stemmed originally from the fairly large cost differential between these steels and steels for through hardening. Also, the hardness that can be achieved with case-hardening is in the range of 58–60 Rc, compared with 49–51 Rc with the now commonly used through-hardening steels. This gives it superior wear characteristics; also, it permits better and longer lasting high polish of the molding surfaces. However, there is the added cost of the carburizing process, which adds carbon to a specified depth (usually from 1.0 to 1.5 mm) and changes the surface to a through-hardening steel. (The base below the skin is usually in the order of 25–40 Rc, according to the selected steel.) Today, many components that were at one time made from case-hardening steels are made from through-hardening tool steels. Many molds for the inherently abrasive thermosets are made from case-hardening steels.

Case-hardening steels are still used frequently for hobbings. The hobbing process is used mainly for the manufacture of cavities with very delicate and difficult shapes, such as knurls and decorative patterns, that would be hard to machine from a solid. A plug, or "hob", is machined from a very tough tool steel to the outside shape of the finished plastic product, and then hardened and well polished. A soft, case-hardening steel blank is then placed in a steel chase, and the hob is pushed into the highly polished surface of the blank by forces of thousands of tons, depending on the size of the hob.

One hob can often be used for a large number of blanks before it wears out. The cavities created in the blanks are practically identical and usually need no further polishing. After removing the hobbed blank from the chase, it must be machined, heat treated, and ground to fit the mold shoe.

This method of mass producing cavities for screw caps, etc., is still quite common, although it too is being replaced in some cases by new processes, such as spark erosion machining (EDM) and precision casting. These processes provide through-hardening tool steel cavities.

Electroforming is another method used, instead of hobbing, for long, thin shapes such as pen barrels. The process is essentially a nickel plating process that deposits a heavy skin, or "tubing", on a master pin, or "mandrel", which has the shape and finish of the final product. The hard metal laid on is a few millimeters thick; the "tubing" must be backed up by a tool steel sleeve.

Through-hardening tool steel is by far the most common material for cavities and cores used today. There are quite a variety of tool steels available from the manufacturers of specialty tool steels that are suitable for the various mold components and molding materials. Some are better than others for certain applications; however, it has been the practice of most moldmakers to standardize on a few, selected types, which can then be stored in the plant or stored by the supplier in certain sizes for the shortest deliveries. While this means in some cases that certain, often minor, advantages of special alloys are being sacrificed, the greatest gain of such standardization is the ready availability of the selected materials and the familiarity of the machinists (time-saving) with the selected small number of steels.

Today, for cavity and core work most moldmakers use "hot-die" steels, which are fairly tough, have good distortion resistance in heat treat, and permit very good polish. Other steels used have special characteristics, such as resistance to wear, or are especially tough against deformation. In all, there are about a dozen steels which provide all characteristics required for the average mold.

Tungsten-carbide alloys are sometimes used for long, slender cores. They are two to three times as stiff (against deflection) as steel, and their heat conductivity is better than steel. The reasons they are used only rarely are their inherent brittleness (low resistance against shocks), the difficulties in their manufacture, and their high cost.

Stainless steels (SS) are used for essential components in molds for use with corrosive materials, such as PVC, which must be protected from the corrosive action of gases (hydrochloric acid, etc.) escaping during the molding process. (This protection also can be provided by chrome plating of the portions exposed to corrosion .) SS in the "420" group can be hardened to approximately 50–52 Rc; in the "440C" group, to 56–58 Rc. Occasionally, the whole mold (i.e., all plates) is made from SS.

4.6.1 Terminology of Materials

Modulus of elasticity is a measure of stiffness of any material. All steels have approximately the same modulus, whether mild steel or hardened tool steel. This must not be confused with tensile strength, which is a measure of the resistance against fracture. Any material, when stressed below its elastic (or yield) limit, will return to its original form when the stress is removed. For relatively brittle materials, such as hardened steels, the yield and the tensile strength are about the same. For ductile materials, such as mild steel or aluminum, yield and tensile strength can be much less. Modulus of elasticity, elastic limit, and tensile strength of most nonferrous mold materials are considerably less than those for steel; the values can be found in handbooks on materials.

The mold shoe is the portion of the mold that is not in contact with the plastic material. Generally, mild steel was and is still used for cheaper molds, but for any quality mold with a long life planned, prehardened steels should be used because they can usually be machined easier and faster and are less prone to damage in handling. The additional cost of the steel is only a small fraction of the total mold cost. As a general rule, the total cost of all materials in a mold is only about 15% of the total mold cost.

In some cases, the mold shoe plates are made from SS to protect them against the corrosion by the molding materials, particularly PVC, and sometimes just from corrosion due to the humidity in the plant. As an alternative to the use of SS plates, the mold shoe plates can be plated.

Electroless nickel plating protects not only the outside of the plates but also penetrates to some extent the cooling lines and all other holes drilled in the plates. Some molders paint the mold plates on the outside, which is not very effective as protection against corrosion, especially between the plates.

4.7 Automatic Molds

Molding operations originally consisted of molding machines, molds, and, for every machine, an operators whose job it was to open the safety gate after every cycle, remove the products and runners, and initiate the next cycle by closing the gate or by pushing the mold-close button of the machine. Usually, in older injection molds with cold runners, the sprue was connected in such a way to a sprue puller that it had to be removed by hand. Often, products were only partially ejected and were still hanging on the cores from where they had to be removed. In thermoset molding, the operator had to load the cavities or the shooting pot of transfer molds and then remove the products.

First in thermoset molding, and then in thermoplastic molding, efforts were concentrated on eliminating the need for the operator at the machine. Usually, the mold design changes required were not extensive. The advantages were not only in the saving of the operator's time but also in the improvement of product quality because the cycle time from shot to shot became constant, rather than dependent on the operator's skill.

The operation of thermoset molds was automated with mechanical loading boards for the preheated pellets (or for loading the molding powder) and with automatic unloading trays to remove the products. Also automated were air blasts and brushes for the cleaning action. The only difference automation made to the molds was usually the requirement for a longer ejection stroke to permit the unloading trays to enter between the ejected products and the top of the mold.

For thermoplastics, there are usually few differences between an automatic and a nonautomatic mold; the differences are mostly in the ejection of the runner systems. In 2-plate molds, the design of the sprue puller is such that the sprue will be positively ejected. In 3-plate molds, the runner system is such that the sprue is completely (not just partly) pulled out from the sprue bushing or, if a hot sprue is used, the cold sprue is eliminated altogether. Also, the mold plates must separate far enough for the runner system to fall free and not hang up between the plates. Some molders use special, automatic runner removal systems to eliminate any chance of the runners hanging up in the mold.

The ejector pins must be flush with the products, or even a little short, to avoid being embedded into the product, which would prevent it from falling free. Also, the stroke of the ejectors or the stripper plate must be long enough to ensure that the products can fall free without hanging up on other cores, ejectors, or leader pins. In some cases, the use of a well-directed air blast under the products or a down-draft air stream, or air "curtain", will ensure that the products clear the molding area. Two-stage ejection is also used to ensure complete ejection.

Once the runners and products are cleanly ejected, there is no problem in having the machine recycle automatically, thus creating a fully automatic operation.

In some cases, "ejection protection" is used to monitor the clearing of the mold before the signal for recycling is given. This can be of great advantage in the molding of delicate products where hang-ups are easily possible and where a product remaining in the cavity or on the core could cause serious damage to the mold when clamped up. Unfortunately, such monitoring by product weight, light screen, or by other, more sophisticated methods requires time and causes a slow down of the operation. It is better to ensure that products are ejecting well rather than to introduce more equipment, which usually means added sources of potential troubles.

Occasionally, from the point of view of automatic operation, it is not desired to have the products fully ejected but to relegate the final ejection to a positive take-off mechanism or to a guide rail mechanism. This can be achieved by leaving some of the ejectors slightly embedded in the products. In such cases, the mold will not operate fully automatically unless the take-off or guide rail mechanism is operative.

In general, there is little, if any, difference between automatic or nonautomatic molds. There are, however, exceptions in cases where the product design requires the use of internal or external side cores, etc. The decision may then be made to build a nonautomatic mold and employ an operator for product removal rather than to complicate the mold construction beyond economical reason. In such cases, consideration should also be given to slower, external automatic product removal systems ("robots") as a viable alternative.

4.8 Mold Design, Drawings, Standards

In the early days of this industry, the mold design was done by the molders, who were often tool makers as well. No formal drawings were prepared; the designs remained in the tool maker's head or enough information was put on scraps of paper for the tool maker and his helpers to understand.

As the technology developed, a necessary division between the molder and the tool maker—by then, the moldmaker—required a more formal approach. The molder submitted his request to the moldmaker, who prepared a simple assembly drawing showing the general layout of the mold to be built with some dimensions indicated. More sophisticated molders had their own design departments to prepare such assembly drawings, which specified what the molder expected and which could then also be used to get competitive quotations.

The detailed design of the cavities and cores and, generally, the construction of the mold were left to the moldmaker. He would, in his drawing office, either break down the assembly drawing into detail drawings, which were then processed through the moldmaker's plant, or the shop foreman would use the assembly drawing directly by outlining to the various machinists in the shop what was required. Again, much detailed information was given out by informal scraps of paper and by word of mouth.

Material specifications were often included in the assembly drawing or were (at least partly) left to the moldmaker's discretion. The only important limitations given were the size and specifications of the molding machine(s) into which the mold was to fit.

Gating, cooling, venting, and other mold features, which today are recognized as crucial and on which the productivity of a mold depends, were taken care of as rather unimportant details, and were left to the decision of the moldmaker, with rarely anyone understanding their importance.

It was this same moldmaker who then had the responsibility to assemble the mold by fitting the various components and to try out the mold for its function. The moldmaker mainly checked to see if the product dimensions were correct but had little concern regarding the molding functions, let alone productivity. Any further work to improve the mold (added venting, better ejection, etc.) was then the responsibility of the molder.

This state of affairs became very unsatisfactory, especially if additional molds were required because of increasing production. Interchangeability of parts between molds of identical designs could not be accomplished. Improvements of the designs to provide better performance based on newly discovered or disclosed information could not be incorporated.

Another factor was the ever-increasing demand for molds as the industry grew larger and larger, and the lack of qualified moldmakers to build molds by the old methods. The moldmaker's main function was to fit the mold parts to each other, even though they were not quite accurate. While it took many years to become a qualified moldmaker, machinists could be trained relatively fast in their specific areas.

Thus, the "engineered" mold came of age. The assembly (design) drawing became an important basis for the mold, to be scrutinized by the "practical persons" experienced in the operation of the mold and in the various machining operations necessary to build it, but it also was closely examined by qualified engineers who made their contribution to the design based on solid engineering considerations. This practice was applied to develop improved methods of bringing the molding material to the cavities, more efficient cooling and venting, better selection of materials, newer mold mechanisms for improved mold safety, and better methods of production and automation.

An immediate and direct result of this method of mold engineering was the need for detail drawings to show necessary and practical tolerances for all dimensions and exact specifications for each component so that the mold parts could be produced by machinists with no experience at all in moldmaking. Their only concern was to produce the part to match the drawing; the actual building of molds was left to mold assemblers, who did not necessarily have to be moldmakers because the parts they assembled needed no adjustments.

This also permitted interchangeability of components and practically eliminated (except in rare and unavoidable cases) the "fitting" of components. It also permitted the use of spare parts, which could be supplied either with the molds or later. Mold engineering also made redesigns possible without major changes to the mold and without requiring parts to be fitted, provided the mold was correctly built to the drawing specifications and any changes during and after the building of the mold were properly recorded.

Through this engineering method, the responsibility for the performance of the mold was squarely put on the mold designers. The portion of the mold cost attributable to mold design increased dramatically from practically nothing, when the toolmaker built the mold, to a hefty 15–25% of the total mold cost. The design and engineering cost includes all the assembly and detail drawings, and the bill of materials. It should be recognized, however, that this cost is incurred only once for a mold and will not be repeated if two or more molds are to be built from the same set of drawings, except possibly for some administrative charges.

Design standards are the next step toward advancement in the industry. It must be the endeavor of a good mold designer to reuse, as much as possible, previously used and well-proven mold designs, a practice which leads to the establishment of mold standards. The selection of mold components, hardware, methods of manufacturing, and materials, especially by larger groups of mold designers, is taken away from the individual designer, who may find in many cases different approaches and solutions to the same problems, all of which may be right. Instead, such mold standards provide one practical solution for each problem, thereby saving the designer time and also facilitating work in the shop if the same designs and methods are used again and again. Design standards also lend themselves to pre-engineering of many components and permits the stocking of such parts for improved deliveries.

The earliest standards applied mainly to the sizes of mold plates; certain items of hardware, such as leader pins and bushings; ejectors; mounting hardware; and some tools. Gradually, the scope of standardization increased to include mold components; pre-engineered cavity and core blanks; components such as hot runner systems, heaters, and special take-off and ejection mechanisms; as well as monitoring and mold safety provisions.

It should be pointed out that such designs or mold standards can never be rigidly frozen. New technologies, new methods, and new practical experiences will from time to time require that standards be changed, improved, and updated.

Computer-assisted design (CAD) has its greatest advantage in the availability of many standard designs and standard parts in its "memory". It also removes the drudgery of having to draw the same things over and over again.

5 Injection Molding Techniques

5.1 Stack Molding

Stack molds originated in the compression molding of large, flat articles, such as rubber mats, which need high tonnage for molding. To make better use of the available (vertical) molding machines, "stacks" of mold plates, each containing cavities and cores, are positioned one above the other. Lost motion linkages lift each plate approximately the same distance from the next plate to allow the operator to insert the raw rubber and to remove the finished articles. The plates are usually steam-heated. This method allows machines with relatively small platen size and low tonnage to produce the same large number of articles that would normally require production by very large machines if molded in one plane.

The theory behind stack molding is simple (Fig. 5.1). Clamp force, F, equals the sum of the reaction forces, R, in the tie bars and creates the necessary locking force in any mold. If there is more than one set of cavity and core plates (Fig. 5.1 shows two), the sum of the forces, p, in the left core block equals F, and the sum of the forces, p, in the right core block equals the sum of the reaction forces, R. The forces p within the cavity block to the left and to the right balance each other. The effective molding area is doubled, and the rated machine clamp force is available for each set or "stack" of cavities and cores. In some rubber molds, there are as many as ten stacks.

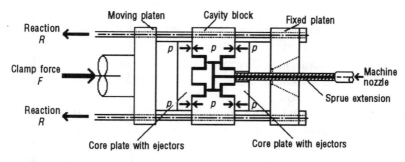

Figure 5.1   Stack mold with two sets of cavity and core plates.

Stack molds were first used in injection molding some 40 years ago in the manufacture of toilet seats and covers. The main reason was the extremely long cycle time for these articles, in addition to the large platen area and tonnage required. The method was simple: The ring-shaped seat was on the injection side so that the sprue could reach through the cavity and its core; the seat cover was then center gated. The cold runner and sprue were manually removed with the products. Today's stack molds are much more sophisticated; they make better use of the molding machine by doubling its available molding area. Stack molding is often selected to produce matching sets of products, such as Petri dish bases and covers, in one mold.

The main reason to use stack molds is that the output of a machine can be practically doubled, therefore requiring less plant space for the same productivity as two machines with single-level molds. The cost of a stack mold is about the same as, or a little less than, two equivalent, single-level molds.

Another advantage of stack molds is color match of assemblies. Since both products (e.g., base and cover) are molded simultaneously, color match is guaranteed.

Stack molds usually cycle almost as fast as if the same products were produced in a single-level mold with a similar cavity layout. The clamp tonnage required is usually about 10% higher, which is due to the fact that the force from the machine nozzle acts on the floating cavity plate and must be taken up by the clamping force.

The ejection on the moving core half may be conventional; on the stationary core half, it may be done by mechanical links with the moving platen or with hydraulically or air-operated ejectors located inside the mold or within the stationary platen. In some molds, a linkage tied in with the opening and spacing of the floating (cavity) plate may be used to operate the ejection mechanism.

Earlier stack molds were cold runner molds, and the products were dropped with the runners. It was quite a problem to make the molds run fully automatically with the runners in both parting lines. Most stack molds built today are hot runner molds, either with long, extended sprue bars fastened to the cavity plate or with valve gated hot sprues arranged in line in the stationary mold half and in the floating plate. This latter method is quite complex but avoids having the sprue bar traverse one mold face. However, since most molds have more than two cavities per face, they can usually be arranged so that the sprue bar does not interfere with the ejection of the products.

All stack molds built today are injected through the stationary platen with a centrally located runner system. However, the mold can also be fed from the side (or top) into the cavity blocks or into the parting lines; this could then be done for more than two levels. In these multilevel systems, the actuation of the many plates presents a problem during the opening, as does the need to space them evenly and to eject the products.

5.2   Blow Molding

The blow molding technique is used whenever the products are of such a design that regular cores which define the inside of the product cannot be withdrawn from the product. This is the case with all bottles and containers for which the neck opening is smaller than the inside of the product. (In some cases, collapsible cores may permit such products to be injection molded.) Large barrels can also be blown, as may certain toys, such as balls, animal shapes, etc., which do not require any opening.

There are two distinct methods of blow molding. Both methods start from a "preform" or "parison" (a term borrowed from the glass industry). The essential differences are described in the sections below.

5.2.1   Extrusion Blow Molding

The first method, extrusion blow molding, starts with an extruded tube of a certain length that is sometimes profiled to best suit the required final shape. While hot, the tube is severed from the extruder and placed in a blow mold. A blow pin is inserted as the mold closes, and high pressure air is blown into the inside of the tube. Because the plastic is still hot, it will expand until it touches the cooled walls of the blow mold, where it then freezes; the so created product is then ejected.

The method is fairly simple and fast. Single or multiple cavities are practical, and the productivity can be quite high. The main problem with this method is that a certain amount of scrap must be removed around the bottle neck and at the bottom. This scrap can usually be reprocessed. The neck finish is often (unavoidably) not as good as desirable for high-quality products.

Some plastics can be processed easily by extrusion blow molding, particularly PVC and PE. Crystal PS and some of the engineering materials, such as PET (the most commonly used plastics for clear containers), cannot be blown from extruded tubing.

Since the process is fairly simple and the tooling is inexpensive, the process lends itself well for low-cost production items and short runs.

5.2.2 Injection Blow Molding

The injection blow molding technique was developed primarily with the intent to eliminate the two main shortcomings of extrusion blow molding (i.e., the trim scrap and the poor quality of the neck finish) and to permit molding of bottles from clear PS and PET.

In this method, the parison is produced in an injection molding machine using a mold that differs from a conventional injection mold mainly in cooling of the cavities and cores. The shape of the parison is such that the core can be withdrawn from it, just as in injection molding. The neck (usually a threaded finish) is as good as any injection molded product. The neck of the resulting preform is cooled, but the rest of the plastic must be blown into its final shape and is not cooled; the hot parison is then transferred by one of a number of methods into the blow mold. The blow cavity is cooled, the blow air is introduced through the core, and the finished part is ejected when stiff enough.

This procedure may sound quite simple, but the actual construction of the (usually multicavity) molds is quite complicated by all the mechanisms needed to transfer the parisons to the blow cavities, the methods used to achieve differential cooling in the parisons and in the cavities, and the methods of ejection. In some cases, all these functions are part of the mold; in other cases, the molding machine performs some of the functions required. In any case, the molds are expensive.

Injection blow molding is primarily used for relatively small, high-quality bottles, such as those required in the cosmetics industry, or whenever a good neck finish is an important requirement. It is also used successfully for open containers, such as plastic drinking cups, which could be molded in conventional injection molds, except that the walls achieved with blow molding can be substantially thinner than with injection molding and are, therefore, lighter without sacrificing any significant properties. Also, the blowing action creates biaxial orientation in the thin wall, which makes it pliable and quite resistant to breakage (see also stretch blow molding). Production requirements must be very high to justify injection blow molding.

5.3 Stretch Blow Molding

We will now consider a bit of theory. Molded plastic consists of long molecules arranged randomly in the hot (amorphous) plastic. While flowing through a narrow gate or through narrow gaps (e.g., between the walls of thin-walled products), the molecules are oriented in the direction of the flow. As the plastic is cooled down, the orientation is "frozen in" and the part remains stronger in the direction of the flow than at right angles to it. If the plastic is also stretched by blowing at right angles to the flow, or by mechanical stretching in the direction of the flow, while the molecules are still randomly arranged before cooling, the molecules will be partly rearranged in the direction of the stretch and remain so after cooling, improving the strength of the part in all directions. The result of stretching is often a dramatic improvement of properties.

Without going into details of the methods, several applications of stretching are described below:

Yarns: The fiber is stretched after extrusion before it cools down, which increases its longitudinal strength.

Sheets: The extruded plastic is stretched not only in the direction of the progression of the sheet but also across that direction. This is called "biaxial" stretching or orientation for a more equal strength in either direction.

Molding: For rotationally symmetrical shapes (cups, bottles, etc.), a similar effect to biaxial stretching can be produced by rotating the core in relation to the cavity during injection before the plastic is fully rigid. While such product conventionally molded would be fairly strong longitudinally, it would have little resistance to crushing forces applied sideways or to internal pressures. When molding with rotation, the strength of the product can be equally good in both directions.

In stretch blow molding, a similar principle is applied to the hot parison before and during blowing. The hot and relatively thick-walled parison is shorter than the finished product and much smaller in diameter. Stretching takes place in two directions—to a lesser degree in the direction of the product length, and much more in the direction across—by blowing. There are certain limitations as to the amount of stretching permissible or practical, but such details would be beyond the scope of this book.

In practice, there are two distinct methods used for stretch blow molding: 1) a single-stage process and 2) a two-stage process.

5.3.1 Single-Stage Process for Stretch Blow Molding

There are several different single-stage systems used. They all have the same production sequence in common, described below, although their mechanical execution may be quite different.

Preforms are molded in an injection mold and then transferred to a heat conditioning setup to achieve a temperature suitable for blowing. The preforms are then introduced into the blow mold, stretched and blown, and the finished products ejected.

The advantage of this method is that it is an in-line process with no intervening storage of unfinished products. It is more energy efficient, since the heat required for the injection molding of the parisons is not completely removed from the products but is partly utilized for the blow cycle. Another advantage is the immediate feedback of possible quality problems. Also, since every injection cavity corresponds to a specific blow cavity, faults can be detected and rectified early.

The system is quite similar to injection blow molding, apart from the heat conditioning and the stretching. There are also some injection blow molds which utilize stretching features without the conditioning step. The disadvantage of some systems is the relatively low output. The blow cycle can usually be four to six times faster than the injection cycle but must be deliberately held to the same speed as the injection cycle.

However, other systems now use injection molds in which the number of cavities is a multiple of the number of blow cavities at a ratio equal to that between injection time and blow time. (For example, with a 24-second injection time and 4-second blow time, the cavity ratio would be 6:1 between injection and blow mold.) A disadvantage is the dependence on the reliability of every portion of the system. If one part goes down, the whole production stops.

5.3.2 Two-Stage Process for Stretch Blow Molding

In this method, the parisons are produced in conventional injection molding machines. After molding, the products are cooled completely and either removed to storage or conveyed directly to specialized "reheat & blow" (R&B) machines. There are several executions of these R&B machines, but the principle is basically the same.

Cold preforms are (automatically) oriented on carriers and transferred to a heating station, where they are heated to blowing temperature. The preforms are then transferred to a blow mold, stretched and blown, and the finished products ejected.

An advantage of a two-stage system is that the parisons can be produced, using the most efficient methods, by specialized, experienced molders. (Molding of preforms from PET is considerably more difficult than conventional plastics molding.)

Another advantage is that preforms can be stored during slack in production, and they permit extensive maintenance or retooling without interruption of production and without taking up much space. Shipping also may be simplified in that preforms, rather than bulky bottles, can be shipped to a user, such as a bottling plant. The blowing set-up is relatively simple and can easily be an in-house process at the bottling plant.

The main disadvantage of this system is the lack of early feedback from the blowing operation. Preforms may appear to be satisfactory when molded but may turn out to be unsuitable for blowing, or they may produce finished products with characteristics below the expected standards. For example, it may take weeks to discover that a certain lot, already shipped, had too high an acetalde-hyde level and that the finished bottles must be scrapped. Another disadvantage is the additional energy required to reheat the preforms for blowing.

5.4 Two-Color, Two-Material Molding

Typical products two-color molding products are two-color escutcheons, type-writer keys, automobile taillight lenses, and items such as drinking cups or mugs with decorations. Three- and four-color products can also be made, although they are rare, as the mold and the equipment required becomes rather compli-cated.

The basic principle is fairly simple, and there are many different methods (and numerous patents) covering this technology. The following example explains the molding of a relatively simple two-color drinking cup.

In this method, shown in Fig. 5.2, the first shot (inside) remains on the core, which is then transferred into the second shot cavity. It should be noted that the second cavity must "shut off" perfectly around the plastic of the first shot (in Fig. 5.2b), around and at the lower end of the rim) to prevent the plastic of the

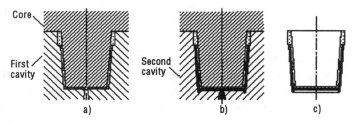

Figure 5.2   Steps in two-color molding: a) first shot (inside color), b) second shot (outsidecolor), and c) finished two-color cup.

second shot covering the plastic from the first shot where it is not desired. To accomplish this, the second cavity must be slightly smaller to allow for shrinkage of the material. Actually, part of the core for the second shot is plastic from the first shot!

The above is a very simple example. Other products may have lettering or ornaments of either the first or second color, and in the worst cases, "islands" such as the inside of the letter "O", "A", etc. These islands require special methods and mold construction for proper filling, not further explained here, and which are the subject of many patents.

In some methods, the products are completely removed from the cores and placed on different cores. In some cases, the outside is shot first and then the inside; in others, it is the other way around. In some arrangements, the repositioning and the injection of both colors occurs within one mold; in others, two separate molds are used in one machine. Such a machine must be equipped with controls for the transfer, such as a rotary shuttle, and with controls for the injection units for each material. Occasionally (earliest methods or experimentally), two separate machines are used side by side, and the products are transferred manually from the first mold into the second.

Creating a product with three or four colors requires a third or fourth injection unit to be tied in with the machine and requires much more complicated molds and transfer mechanism controls.

Note that both the materials need not be of the same type, but they must be compatible; also, they must be able to sustain the injection pressures at the second shot without melting or deformation. It is also desirable to use low shrinkage materials; high shrinkage tends to pull and separate the two layers.

It is questionable whether the first and second shot really bond or the two layers adhere to each other just due to the effect of vacuum—that, in fact, the atmospheric pressure holds them together. This is really immaterial as long as the layers stay together; however, sometimes, as in the design of typewriter keys, a number of projections are molded in the first shot which are then embedded into or fused by the second shot to assure better bonding.

Typical examples of products which consist of two entirely different materials are:

1. A spatula for kitchen use: The very soft and pliable flat portion of the spatula is molded over the end of the hard handle. The assembly is held together only by some gripping serrations in the handle.
2. Lead acid battery plates: To substantially reduce the weight of the batteries, which consist of a number of such plates, a grid of lead is supported by a superimposed grid of polypropylene. This shows that

even plastics and metals can be molded and combined by means of the two-color principle. The holding between the two materials was effected by a special, patented method of loops molded into the plastic in only a few locations as it flows around the lead.

The method of gating is usually determined by the size of the article. Larger parts can be hot runnered, both in the first and in the second shot. Smaller parts are usually produced with two- or 3-plate systems. If the products are transferred to different cores, they are kept on the runners, which are then used as "fixtures" for handling the transfer. Sometimes, special transfer mechanisms are used.

5.5 Co-Injection Molding

This is a relatively new two-material process, and the principle is quite simple (Fig. 5.3). An exactly measured shot of the first material is first injected into a cold mold so that the mold is not filled Fig. 5.3a). A second shot, from the second injection unit, then enters inside the first material and almost fills the cavity (Fig. 5.3b). Finally, the first material is again injected to fill the cavity and to seal the gate (Fig. 5.3c). Most of the problems in this technology center around supplying the materials from the injection units, gating, and valving. Of course, hot runnering is very important and adds to the complications.

This method is being used for two distinct applications:

1. Large housings and furniture panels: The inside material contains a foaming agent; the resulting product has a typical injection-molded skin and a foamed core. In a way, the parts resemble structural foam (low-pressure) moldings and have their weight advantages; however, the appearance (finish) is much better and is similar to an injection molded finish. The biggest advantage is, therefore, that these parts don't need painting.

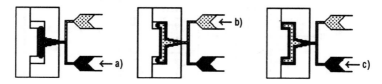

Figure 5.3   Co-injection sequence: a) first shot (cold), b) second shot inside first material, and c) first material fills cavity.

2. Preforms. An other application is the molding of products such as bottle preforms which can be produced with the skin of a generally low cost material to provide the necessary strength while the inside, made from rather expensive material, has the necessary barrier properties.

A similar process may be used with more than two different materials, with correspondingly increased technical difficulties.

5.6 Turret Molding

The turret system is a further development of the principle of using (usually) two injection units on one clamp. In the earlier-described two-color molding method, both injection units are on the same side, and the molds (or products) are shuttled (transferred) in one plane (Fig. 5.4). In the turret system, the injection units are at opposite sides of the machine, and the mold cores are mounted on a rotating "turret" so that the first shot is injected similarly to conventional molding, but the second shot is injected from the opposite side. Between the two injection cycles, the mold opens and permits the turret with the mold cores to rotate 180° before the molds reclose (Fig. 5.5).

Comparison of Fig. 5.4 and 5.5 shows the obvious difference between these systems. In the first, the axis of rotation of the cores is in line with the center of the clamp; in the second, it is at right angles. The axis can be either horizontal (as shown) or vertical; the choice depends on various alternative requirements, such as the method of ejection (or take-off) after molding and the convenience in the overall layout of the machine.

It should be noted that the second injection unit must travel with the moving platen (as shown); it could also be stationary but must then be brought into

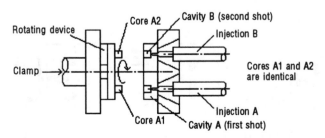

Figure 5.4   Two-color molding machine.

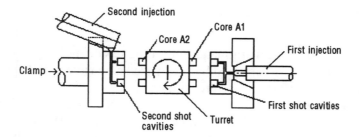

Figure 5.5   Two-color turret molding machine with two positions.

engagement with the second cavity mold half as it arrives in the mold-closed position.

A turret system may be designed to stop in four positions rather than two (Fig. 5.6). Although Fig. 5.6 shows two injection systems, a turret machine may also have only a conventional injection unit, while the turret may be used for the performance of other operations. In such cases, it is used just like a repositioning device to move the cores through a succession of stations, each for a different task.

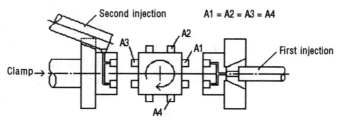

Figure 5.6   Turret molding machine with four positions.

For example, the first position could be for injection, and the second and third used only for prolonged cooling, before the product is ejected at the fourth station. In other arrangements, the third station could be used for gate cutting, for marking, for placing of inserts onto the core, etc. The turret could also have more than four stations, but for practical reasons four is a preferred arrangement.

It is important that the clamping force is taken up by the mold in the first and the (opposing) third stations, which are in line. The turret itself cannot be made strong enough without backing from the other side to clamp the injection cavity and core during injection.

The speed of operation is not a problem. The earlier-mentioned two-material system for battery plates runs on a three-second cycle.

5.7 Multiple Station Molding

The multiple station system originated with compression molding of small parts, such as thermoset screw caps, and has been used extensively in the production of large runs. Up to 50 stations were common.

The principle underlying this method is that loading of the cavities (with thermosets) or injection (with thermoplastics) takes only a fraction of the time required, respectively, to cure or cool the molded products. Originally, a number of small, identical molds, each with only one or a very small number of cavities, were placed on a turn table.

With thermosets, the heated mold is open in the loading position. After the plastic is loaded, the table moves to the next position, where the mold is clamped, and curing starts. After passing through several steps in which the cavities are kept clamped, they then continue step by step around the circle until the products are cured. Products are ejected as the mold opens, before arriving at the loading position. With thermoplastics, the process is similar, except that the cavities are cooled, and the plastic is injected into the closed mold.

Lately, the same method has also been used for short runs by installing molds for different parts into the "round table". The loading (or injecting) must be so controlled that the quantity of the supplied material matches each different mold as it comes to the loading station. The main reasoning behind this method was that very small molds, which are fast to produce, could be run experimentally or in pilot production very shortly after the requirements for certain new parts arose without need for investing in large molds. If the quantities increased, more similar molds could then be installed in the machine. Of course, with today's technology and probably because of more reliable market analyses, such "tentative" methods are not commonly used.

There is a notable exception, however, where the multistation machine is still widely used— namely, when inserts are supplied at one station in the table, and the plastic is then "shot around" the insert. The manufacture of tooth paste tubes is a typical application in which separately made multilayered cylindrical tube sections are first loaded, and then the top, including the threaded tip, is injection molded onto it.

Multiple station machines are very common in shoe manufacturing, where the entire shoe, or only the plastic portion of the shoe (sole), is molded onto the inserted cloth upper shoe.

5.8   Shuttle (Insert) Molding

This method is widely used for the molding of plastic around inserts that require manual loading into the mold, such as electric connectors, that are to be surrounded by insulating materials. The manual operation is selected either because of the difficulties connected with automatic inserting or because it is not economically viable to automate, in case of small production requirements.

The principal feature of such a set-up is a mold that consists of a cavity on the injection side and a pair of identical core halves, which are mounted on a slide, or "shuttle", on the ejection side. While one core with the inserts is in the molding position, the operator installs the inserts into the other core for the next shot. As the mold opens after the plastic is cooled (or cured, with thermosets), the operator slides the core that contains the inserts into the molding position, the mold closes, and, after removing the finished products, the operator again prepares the core for the next shot.

Preferably, a machine used for such manual operation has a vertical clamp so that inserting may take place at table height in front of a seated operator, and the inserts are held by gravity in position. It may be useful to shuttle the cavities and have only one core; this is of special advantage with thermosets, where the plastic can then be easily loaded by utilizing gravity.

5.9   Insert Molding

As a general rule, it is advantageous to avoid inserts. This can often be done by appropriate product design and careful selection of materials; for example, the plastic may be chosen to be strong enough to perform the function of an insert. A typical example is the molded "live hinge" joining a PP box and lid so that it is not necessary to later add a metal hinge. If this is not possible, as for example with inserts that are to conduct electricity, the products should be so designed that these inserts can be assembled after molding.

By adhering to this rule, the mold can be designed to run in the most efficient way, without loss of molding cycle speed and without compromising the cavity layout to accommodate the inserts. Inserting anything into an open mold will result in a slow down of the operation by adding to the mold open time. Manual inserting was covered in Section 5.8 above and is not practical, and certainly not safe, unless the rather slow method of shuttle molding is selected.

Insert molding in a conventional system (horizontal machine) should never be attempted unless the machine is equipped with a fully automatic loading device so that the operator never needs to reach into the molding area during a production run. The inserting mechanism or the mold (or both) must be equipped with sensors or other alarm provisions to make sure that not only it is safe to close the mold without colliding with the mechanism but also that all the inserts are properly placed before the next cycle can start.

The number of possibilities for inserting is practically unlimited, but due to the unavoidable complications within the mold, the specially built inserting mechanism, and the necessary safeguards, which all add a hefty sum to the mold cost, it is little wonder that relatively few molds utilize automatic inserting unless the productivity to be achieved is very high and worth the added cost, or other compelling reasons exist.

One of these "other" reasons is the use of paper (cardboard) inserts, which results in "finishing" the product within the mold by using printed paper so that printing or decorating after molding becomes unnecessary. The inserted paper may also partly take over the function of the product, which otherwise would have to be assumed by a much more expensive plastic.

Typical examples of products using one or both of these reasons are oil cans, made from "cheap" cylindrical preprinted paper tubing with a plastic bottom molded onto it, or surgical trays, which consist mainly of plain cardboard folded within the mold as the mold closes and joined at all the edges with plastic during the injection process. In both these examples, the savings of plastic are considerable. There are many other such products (e.g., in food packaging).

Other inserts that can be placed into molds are metals (for reinforcements, hinges, pins, etc.) and plastic products molded from materials that can perform as metal inserts. But, as mentioned in the beginning, it is preferable if such products can be assembled after the molding.

5.10 In-Mold Decorating

Many plastic products are decorated after molding by printing, silk screening, or other methods. This requires additional handling and, in some cases, also preparation of the surface to be decorated so that the inks will adhere to the plastic. Such decoration is often satisfactory; however, a better finish may be desirable in some cases. This can be created by inserts, preprinted on a moldable material, which must be compatible with the base material of the finished product.

Again, the technology originated with the (thermoset) compression molding of quality dinnerware made mostly of urea-formaldehyde, etc. The process is quite simple. Blanks are preprinted by a high-quality multicolor printing process using half-tone lithography. The mold (in a vertical machine) is loaded with the plastic, closed, and curing is started. When the plastic is almost cured, the mold is opened, the printed blank is inserted, and the mold is reclosed to finish the curing cycle. During this time, the printed blank joins the base plastic, but the inks remain on the surface of the product. The finished products then display a decoration that is much superior in appearance to conventional printing, and the surface is also highly resistant to wear.

Similar methods have been used in injection molding. However, the cost factor appears to make this process uneconomical. In molding a dinner plate, the normal molding cycle is about one minute or more, and the time required for the inserting is only a few seconds; this does not add substantially to the product's cost. Also, in such a compression molding set-up, the operator has enough time to serve two or more machines.

With injection molding, the process is somewhat different. The blank must be inserted prior to the closing of the clamp and injection. This requires all the complications in the mold and in the machine explained in Section 5.9, Insert Molding, above. In many methods, the inserting adds to the molding cycle, as it takes place during the mold-open time. There are, however, processes (e.g., Cerbo) where the paper insert is prepositioned during the molding cycle above the cavity. As the mold opens and the molded products pull out with the core prior to ejection, the new inserts slide into position in front of the cavity, ready to be pushed into it by the core as the mold recloses. This is done without loss of cycle time.

There are other methods of in-mold decorating, but they will not discussed here.

6 Automatic Product Handling

There are several reasons for introducing automatic product handling into the molding plant. The main reason is the trend toward gradual reduction, if not complete elimination, of the need for operators to do repetitive work associated with mass production. Another reason is the improvement of product quality. Manual operation of the machines and manual product handling has brought about a lax attitude toward the quality of molds and the reliability of machines by relying on the operator to make corrections whenever ejection or filling problems arise. This tends to create wide fluctuations in product quality and in the output of molds and machines.

With better mold designs and construction, and also with better machines and controls, the output of a system (mold plus machine) can be improved and automatic molding made possible. Also, some products must not be touched by hands to maintain the inherent sterility of the products as they come out of the mold.

An important reason for automated handling is the need to maintain the orientation required in subsequent operations; in other words, the products should not drop randomly as they come out of the mold but should transfer in an orderly fashion, either directly ("in-line") or via "oriented storage", such as in specially designed holding trays or boxes, to their next destination, which may be printing, assembling, loading, or other operations.

Quality and quantity control can also become part of the automated handling by the checking of products during the removal operation either just for their presence in the take-off mechanism or for specific dimensions. Such checking can consist of detecting faults as they occur and feeding the information back to the machine for automatic correction, or it can merely stop the operation and sound an alarm.

Some methods of automatic parts removal have been used for a long time in the molding of thermoset articles, but that concern was mainly with the automatic unloading of the products, which then have to be tumbled for deflashing and thereby lose their orientation. Another old method of automatic unloading is used when "pressing" compression-molded audio records, where the molded disks are removed by a take-off using the peripheral flash as a "handle". The records are automatically placed on a turntable and the flash removed with a stationary knife as the record rotates. Another take-off, using vacuum to handle the record, takes the finished article away.

A number of different product handling methods exist for injection molding, both for thermosets and thermoplastics. Many such methods were pioneered by Husky and are still presently producing as very efficient systems.

6.1 Runner Removal

This method is a forerunner of a true product removal system. The necessity for runner removal stemmed from the need for certainty that the runners of a 3-plate mold are ejected before the machine can recycle. A cam or hydraulically operated mechanical arm with a wiper passes through the gap were the 3-plate runner is ejected and makes sure that the runner has not remained there, possibly hung-up due to poor ejection or due to stringing from the nozzle. Sensors make sure that the arm has returned before restarting the next cycle.

A similar method that wipes across the face of the mold with a mold wiper (brush) is used occasionally to ensure that the ejected products (and the runners, in case of a 2-plate mold) have cleared the molding area. This is of special interest if the molded products are very small and may stick to the mold surface by static electricity or if there is a flash or stringing present that may prevent them from falling.

A variation of the mold wiper is an arm equipped with a gripper, which grabs the sprue or the runner for its removal. This system will also work with 2-plate molds and can also remove the runner with the products still attached to it for oriented removal of the products to a downstream operation; the runner-products assembly is then deposited alongside the machine, usually on a conveyor.

The products still attached to the runners are ejected as one unit and fall from the mold onto a conveyor to move it to a packing station, where they are degated and placed into suitable boxes, oriented as they come from the mold. In some cases, for example in some toys, the products are deliberately left on the runners and shipped to the ultimate user, who separates the products.

6.2 Oriented Products Removal

The term "oriented removal" is used if the products are "grabbed" by a handling system before they have lost the position they had in the mold. Grabbing can be achieved mechanically with air-operated claws or spring clips, with vacuum, or with compressed air fed into expandable tubing surrounding the molded product. The products are kept in their "as molded" relationship until placed into the next step in the manufacturing process without losing their orientation.

The next step may be an assembly operation. For example, the two halves of an assembly may be molded side by side and then assembled, either while still in the take-off mechanism or in a downstream operation (i.e., audio or video cassette boxes). The orientation may be required as the products reach the packaging station and are loaded into boxes (i.e., typewriter ribbon cases). In other systems, the products may be placed into holding fixtures, such as drawers or trays, which are then transferred to storage or in-line to the next step in the manufacture (i.e., 3.5-in. computer disk boxes).

6.2.1 Take-Off Methods

Two basically different methods are used for the above described automatic products removal systems:

1. The mechanism is tied in with the motion of the machine. The big advantage of this system is that no time is added to the cycle time, as compared to the operation of the same mold without take-off. As the mold opens, a take-off arm with grippers for the products moves into the molding area to face the cores. While the machine is still opening, the products are ejected into the grippers. As the machine closes, the take-off arm with the products held by the grippers is moved outside the molding area. The products can be removed while the mold is closed, either directly or using a secondary transfer mechanism, and the products may then drop onto conveyors that remove the (still oriented) products to their next destination. The transfer mechanism can also be equipped to assemble the products before depositing them. There is perfect synchronism between the motions of the machine and the take-off, and no safeguards are required to keep the moving mold and the take-off from colliding.

   This system is very efficient, since the take-off occurs during the dry cycle time of the machine. Its limitations are spatial restrictions and strength of the cam mechanism operating the take-off arm. This, and weight limitation to keep the moving masses low, prevents its use for relatively long or heavy parts.

2. The mechanism operates independently. Such take-off requires that the mold be open, or almost open, before the take-off mechanism may enter the molding area to avoid collisions between the take-off mechanism and the mold. This delay in time adds to the molding cycle. The motions required are usually provided by hydraulic cylinders, which allow better control than air cylinders; they also require electric switching and valving, which adds more time to the cycle. The mechanism also requires sensors to prevent collisions between the moving parts.

The added time is only significant if the product could otherwise be cycled very fast. With products requiring molding cycles of five seconds or less, the loss in productivity could be serious; with longer molding cycles, as for PET preforms, such time loss is of minor importance. In addition to being universal in the range of applications, there is the advantage that the speed of the motions can be controlled closely. This is important because the mass of some more complicated gripper and transfer plates may be so large that the desired speeds could create acceleration and deceleration forces beyond the strength and rigidity of the take-off mechanism.

There is no doubt that the trend in this industry is more and more toward automation. Eventually, it will not only be economical for articles with very large production runs but also for shorter run production.

6.3 Controlled Ejection

This methods differs from oriented products removal by the fact that the attitude of the product is not necessarily maintained in its in-mold position; however, the products are not free to tumble or to mix in a random manner. The method is not new. In the early stages of automatic molding of large, relatively flat parts, the molding machine was adjusted so that it opened only far enough to permit the products to slide down between the mold faces after ejection and to end up flat on a conveyor belt. Round products are free to rotate and may thereby lose their relative orientation; products with straight sides could maintain their orientation.

This principle of guiding the products out of the mold area was improved by the addition to the mold itself of a mechanism that moves during the opening stroke to enclose the products from two sides and thereby to provide slides which guide products toward a conveyor or directly into storage trays. During the mold-closing stroke, the slides retract. The slides can also be used to strip the parts from the ejector pins if designed to prevent the products from following the ejector pins as they retract.

This method usually does not add to the molding cycle. The slides are operated by cams tied in with the motion of the mold. Another important advantage of this method is that it can be very effectively and simply used with stack molds; the take-off mechanisms usually require much opening stroke of the mold.

An early, typical application was the molding of Petri dishes where the controlled ejection permitted a simple method of supplying both the base and the cover directly in their proper attitude from the mold to the assembly machine. Other applications are the removal of small, rectangular products, such as cassette bodies, to conveyors, which bring the products to assembly, packaging, or to storage boxes that maintain their orientation.

6.4 Quality Control

This step is mentioned here because of the opportunity offered by orderly products removal to the manufacturing process. Quality control (or inspection) is based either on 100% inspection, which is rarely used in mass production (some medical products excepted), or statistical inspection, which is performed by sampling only a certain percentage of the production. Total production is permitted to have a specified maximum number of bad products.

Quality control is accomplished by inspection from time to time of a specified number of a batch of products made, and the establishment of the number of rejects permitted in that batch. If the percentage of rejects is lower than permitted, it is assumed that the unchecked bulk of the production is also within specification. If it is higher, the production is stopped, and all products produced since the last approved inspection are also rejected.

We will not enter into the mathematical theory of statistical inspection methods. It can easily be seen that the more critical the quality of the end product, the more severe the inspection must be. Oriented product removal provides the opportunity of incorporating an automatic inspection system in-line with the flow of the ejected products, which are at this point either fully oriented or at least in such orderly array that electronic or other inspection systems can be used for 100% of the parts.

References

Books:

Modern Plastics Encyclopedia . New York: McGraw-Hill.

Rubin, I. I. *Injection Molding: Theory and Practice*. New York: J. Wiley & Sons, 1972.

Menges, G.; Mohren, P. *How to Make Injection Molds*. 2nd Edition. Munich: Hanser Publishers, 1992.

Injection Molding Operations—A manufacturing plan. Bolton, Ontario: Husky Injection Molding Systems Ltd., 1980.

Gastrow, H. *Injection Molds—108 Proven Designs*. 2nd Edition. Munich: Hanser Publishers, 1992.

Magazines:

Modern Plastics

Plastics Technology

Plastics Machinery and Equipment

Canadian Plastics

Kunststoffe (German, with some articles translated into English)

Other Recommended Sources for Data:

Machine builders' advertisements and sales literature

Materials suppliers' sales literature and publications

Steel and metal manufacturers' specifications and publications

Index